'Go back, Cassie.'

There was a harsh, mocking inflexion in Ryker's voice as he moved away from her. She was bereft, stunned. 'Tell Jim Harker that there's no deal. No story.'

Cassie closed her eyes, absorbing the impact of the shock on her bewildered senses. When would she ever learn the lesson he had been trying to teach her throughout all those long, empty years? He did not want her. He would never want her.

Dear Reader

As the dark winter nights unfold, what better to turn to than a heart-warming Mills & Boon! As usual, we bring you a selection of books which take you all over the world, with heroines you like and heroes you would love to be with! So take a flight of fancy away from everyday life to the wonderful world of Mills & Boon—you'll be glad you did.

The Editor

When **Joanna Neil** discovered Mills & Boon, her lifelong addiction to reading crystallised into an exciting new career—writing romances. Always prey to a self-indulgent imagination, she loved to give free rein to her characters, who were probably the outcome of her varied lifestyle. She has been a clerk, telephonist, typist, nurse and infant teacher. She enjoys dressmaking and cooking at her Leicestershire home. Her family includes a husband, son and daughter, an exuberant yellow Labrador, and two slightly crazed cockatiels.

FLAME OF
LOVE

BY
JOANNA NEIL

MILLS & BOON

MILLS & BOON LIMITED
ETON HOUSE, 18-24 PARADISE ROAD
RICHMOND, SURREY TW9 1SR

*First published in Great Britain 1993
by Mills & Boon Limited*

© Joanna Neil 1993

*Australian copyright 1993
Philippine copyright 1994
This edition 1994*

ISBN 0 263 78308 1

*Set in Times Roman 11 on 12 pt.
91-9402-48091 C*

Made and printed in Great Britain

CHAPTER ONE

'I WANT to come in. Open up.'

The voice was strong and deep, and even though it was distorted by the heavy wood panelling of the front door the sound of it floated upwards and filtered through to the room where Cassie sat, bare feet curled up beneath her on the makeshift bed.

Someone would deal with it, she decided, going back to her writing.

'I have to talk to you, all of you,' the man insisted.

A commotion had started up downstairs, and through it she strained to hear the muffled reply. Some kind of heated exchange was going on, but they wouldn't let him in; whoever he was, he was wasting his time.

They were worried about the bailiffs for a start, and, with one thing and another, there had been enough trouble over the last few days. They simply weren't taking any risks.

She stretched her legs, easing them into a more comfortable position on the mattress, and settled back, her spine resting against the hard wall, the notepad lying open across her knees. Chewing on the end of her pencil, she idly studied her pink-enamelled toes.

The desire for realism and authenticity was all very well, but she hadn't counted on quite so many disturbances when she had set out to write this article.

A loud hammering started up, the sound of a steel-hard fist meeting up with resistant wood. She could almost feel the reverberations echoing through the house.

'You needn't imagine that I'll go away.' The rumbling tones came again, and she frowned, scoring through the last phrase she had written before checking the watch on her slim wrist.

It was late in the afternoon, so it couldn't be the bailiffs, could it? Anyway, it wasn't likely that they'd be back again, not if Nick's information was right and the police were going to arrive hotfoot in the morning.

The sun streamed in relentlessly through the window and she pushed her fingers through the errant black curls that had escaped from her untidy topknot. Pinning up her long hair made her feel much cooler in this summer heat. It had been just her luck to finish up with the smallest room in the place. If she hadn't been made of sterner stuff, she might almost have begun to feel claustrophobic.

The pounding started up again. 'I know she's in there. I want to talk to her.'

Cassie grinned. It was probably one of Steph's admirers. It wasn't the first time there had been angry spats. He was determined, too, from the sound of him. She opened up the window a notch, allowing the faint breeze to fan her cheeks and throat.

'Patience is not my strong point. You'd do well to think on that.' The gravelled intonation wafted on the air, muted by the clamour that was going on below her in the hall, and a ragged line etched its way into her brow. Wasn't there something vaguely familiar about that voice?

She shrugged dismissively and her oversized T-shirt slid precariously down over her shoulder. Hitching it back into place, she decided that it was times like these when she longed for the privacy of her own flat. The first thing she would do when she went back would be to indulge herself in a long, long soak in the bath.

But work came first. She sighed. Nick was convinced he already had some good photos to send in for the feature. Her mouth quirked wryly. She'd hardly seen him since he'd turned the loft into a dark-room.

'OK, that's it. I'm giving you just five more seconds. One...'

There was a silence.

'Two...'

She held her breath. This man meant business, and he was in a hurry.

'Three...four...'

He wouldn't get through the barricades, would he? She shook her head. Of course he wouldn't.

'Five—stand clear.'

Her mouth gaped a little as the noise of splintering wood gave way to the almighty crash of planking hurling itself to the floor.

'Where is she?' Cold purpose penetrated every syllable, and Cassie's fingers froze on the pencil. She sat up very straight, her face paling with shock. She knew that voice.

Her eyes widened. It couldn't be him, could it? Hadn't he gone over to France just a few weeks ago? He'd said he had some business to sort out over there, that he might extend it to a short holiday. And anyway, he didn't know she was here, did he? How on earth would he have tracked her down? Why would he have wanted to?

Even as she thought it, the knowledge came that anything was possible where he was concerned. The man had his own in-built radar system, didn't he? She flipped her notebook closed and rammed it into her bag on the floor. Pushing her feet into her shoes, she went out on to the landing and surreptitiously peered down over the stair rail.

Studying the newcomer who had erupted with such shattering force into the cramped hallway, she was all too aware that her heart had begun a heavy, discordant pounding against her ribcage, and that her palms were slowly clenching on the wooden rail. It was him all right. Even though he had his back to her, there could be no mistaking him.

Ryker. Six feet two of pure trouble.

There was a clatter in the hall below as someone tripped over what was left of the rough barricade, and Ryker's wide shoulders moved, his unyielding frame tensed, at the ready. The sun's rays lanced through the open doorway, marking him out, touching his crisp black hair with an iridescent gleam.

For a few unguarded moments, Cassie felt the slow, familiar melt of her limbs, the undermining lap at the edges of her resistance. It wasn't fair, this magnetic pull he seemed to exert over her emotions, this way he had of drawing her to him with his own irresistible brand of sorcery. She closed her eyes briefly, fiercely, trying to shut him out. There was no future in loving Ryker. He would never return her feelings.

It was ironic—wasn't it?—that she had spent three years at university trying to get him out of her system—what a futile hope that had been. Her brow furrowed as she tried to clamp down on her wavering thoughts. She wouldn't let his presence cloud her thinking. She had work to do, a feature to write.

Why did he have to turn up here now, when she was in the middle of a scoop? He couldn't just come along and disrupt everything. She hated the thought that he might jeopardise the stand her companions were taking. That was why his sudden arrival had unnerved her, wasn't it? Her inner shakiness had nothing at all to do with fragmented hopes and reckless longings.

Her glance skimmed the small group of men who had assembled in the hallway, and her frown deepened. What were they thinking of, anyway, standing back and letting him through? What was the matter with them? Were their brains completely addled?

All right, so he was a tough-looking proposition, but they didn't know about the black belt in karate, did they? And they outnumbered him three to one, for heaven's sake. They might at least put up some kind of a fight, instead of letting him force his way into the building.

Nick was the first to find his tongue. 'We don't want any trouble, Ryker.'

'Nor do I. If you had let me in I wouldn't have had to resort to force. I have something to say to all of you when I've finished.'

Nick said, 'Couldn't you have waited till tomorrow? Your timing's way out, you know.'

Ryker's impatience showed. 'No, I couldn't.'

He turned to Steph, and Cassie caught the full impact of his hard-boned profile. 'I want Cassandra. Where is she?'

The silly girl went to pieces, her hand riffling through her tousled auburn hair. 'Are you sure?' she said, a funny, breathless little catch in her voice. 'Won't I do instead?'

His mouth curved in brief acknowledgement, and Cassie drummed her fingertips restlessly on the banister. The girl was a fool. Couldn't she see he was lethal? Obviously she didn't know what she was dealing with. The man hadn't stayed a bachelor into his early thirties without knowing how to kiss and run.

Ryker's sharp gaze fastened unerringly on the stairs. 'So there you are,' he said with smooth satisfaction.

'Rats,' she muttered, shooting back into the bedroom. She heard his feet pounding the wooden boards as he took them in ultra-swift time.

Her nerves leapt as he appeared in the doorway, and she stared at him darkly through the sudden wave of dizziness that swirled in her head. He wasn't even breathing fast.

'What are you doing here?' she said directly, striving to keep cool defiance in her tone. It was her only defence against the shock of seeing him standing there, an imposing intruder in the room. She wasn't prepared for it. 'I thought you were in France. You told me you were going away.'

His slow smile did nothing to soothe her prickly emotions. 'But now I'm back,' he murmured. 'And just in time, it seems.'

She scowled. 'Did you *have* to force your way in here like that, like some hot-blooded Viking on the rampage? I'm working, Ryker; this is my territory, and your heavy-handed methods are not wanted here—*you* are not wanted here.'

The snub glanced off his hard exterior. 'So I gather. I've had warmer welcomes than this.' Mockery laced his tone, and she stiffened.

'What did you expect?' she asked grimly. 'I'm in the middle of something. What's behind this sudden appearance? How did you know where I was staying?'

He appraised her thoughtfully. 'This place belongs to a friend of mine. He was planning on making a few renovations, and, to put it mildly, he was less than pleased when he found out about all the activity that had suddenly sprung up. Seeing his property featured in the *Despatch* only intensified his desire to prosecute. Can you blame him?'

Inwardly, Cassie groaned. It couldn't have turned out worse, could it? Her new-found friends had unwittingly focused on the very circles in which Ryker moved. That was bound to mean trouble.

Coolly cynical, he went on, 'I might have guessed from the outset that you and Nick Driscoll had a hand in it. He doesn't change much, does he? The first sniff of opportunity, and he's in there, rooting.'

A tiny muscle flicked in her cheek. 'It's his job. What do you expect?'

'Nothing at all. He doesn't interest me in the slightest.' He stopped moving, his long, hard-muscled body just a hair's breadth away from her, and her eyes were instantly riveted on blue denim pulled taut across strong thighs, on the deep navy sweatshirt that closely moulded his broad chest. Hastily she dragged her gaze away, only to find it meshed with gold as he looked down at her.

'It's your part in it that concerns me,' he said. 'If it had been anyone else, I'd have had no compunction about leaving them to face the consequences. But as things stand, your father is a good friend. He's also a public figure—have you thought about how this could affect him? He isn't likely to react well to your getting yourself mixed up with the police.'

'I have to live my own life, Ryker,' she advised him softly. 'And my father's name isn't going to be drawn into this, so there's no reason for him to get himself into a state. He doesn't need to worry about my every move.'

'Is that so? Maybe he could rest easier if you didn't exhibit such a penchant for the unsavoury. Living in a squat was never going to endear him to your cause, was it?' He paused, a dry smile playing over his firm, well shaped mouth. 'I can't say that your latest crusade came as any great surprise to me when I heard about it, but it did occur to me that you were heading straight for disaster. This particular manoeuvre doesn't appear to have the glow of fortune shining over it.'

Her mouth indented with scornful amusement. 'So I suppose you're here to haul me back into line? What did you have in mind—a brash show of force leading to a tactical surrender of some sort?' She tossed her head, and the unruly cloud of dark curls quivered unsteadily. 'Do us both a favour and take off again, Ryker. I don't need you around. I can sort out my own problems.'

He shifted then, and she watched him warily, his long, vital body an inherent threat to her composure, the shimmering heat of his glance sliding over the ripe softness of her curves. 'Tactical surrender,' he repeated slowly, savouring the words on his tongue, a faint grin in his voice. 'Now there's a thought——'

'Forget it,' she snapped, sharply regretting her unguarded phrasing. 'I'm here, and I'm staying for the duration.'

He watched her consideringly, the warm, speculative gleam still lingering fathoms deep in his eyes. 'An unfortunate stand to take, I'm afraid. You ought to know by now that once I decide on a course of action I always follow it through to its logical conclusion.' He paused to let the message sink in. 'Roughly translated,' he added helpfully, 'that means I'm here now, and I'd like you to leave with me.'

Her smile was deceptively sweet. 'Isn't that too bad? I'm afraid you lost out this time. But put it down to experience, why don't you? After all, things can't always go your way, you know.'

'I wouldn't be too sure about that.' His tawny, tiger eyes mocked her. 'You never did weigh more than a sack of feathers. It wouldn't be the first time I've thrown you over my shoulder.'

Cassie's chin took on an obstinate slant, even as she backed away. Her eyes were a brittle, deep blue. 'You wouldn't dare.'

'Try me,' he challenged drily, eyeing the pert line of her smooth-fitting white jeans.

'Back off, Ryker,' she said, biting down on her uncertainty with an acid tone. 'Lay hands on me and you'll live to regret it. Just remember, you're the one who taught me self-defence, and I sure as hell remember every nasty move in the book.'

'Every one?' he chuckled, moving cl████ ██
I have to see.' Bending suddenly, he swoop██
her unceremoniously over one broad shoul█

Cassie's breath caught in sharp reaction,
senses raggedly absorbing the unexpected contact.
He was all hard-muscled strength; she registered
every tough sinew against the softness of her flesh,
and it was only gradually that her mind began to
function again. He had taken her by surprise; she
had not for one minute thought he would seize her.

Belatedly, she jabbed her fists with full force into
a strategic point along his back. Twisting sharply,
he let her glide to the floor, his arm reaching out
to steady her as she rocked back on her feet.

'Not bad,' he said, his mouth moving in that
crooked, disarming way that made her pulse leap
in frantic haste. 'You'll need to quicken up your
reflexes, though, if you expect to win.'

She swallowed, struggling to regain her composure. As she looked at him, her teeth set in frustration. He was not supposed to find this amusing,
dammit. His grin unsettled her, did alarming things
to the usually even balance of her stomach. It made
her nervous system shoot into overdrive, but she
was darned if she'd give in to it.

She breathed in deeply. 'Look,' she said, 'I'm
sure there are far more important things you could
be doing than trailing around after me. You can
wind down. Go home, and, while you're about it,
tell my father I'm OK, I won't make any sparks,
and he won't find the slightest breath of scandal
attached to his name.'

His features hardened. 'I doubt he would be reassured by your word alone.' Abruptly, he walked away from her, his eyes scanning the room and the landing beyond, and Cassie watched him with smarting resentment. He was determined to interfere, no matter what she said.

He turned back to her. 'What possessed you to come here? This place is a total fire risk, according to the owner. The wiring's in a hazardous condition; there are no decent washing facilities. You don't have to live like this.'

Her look was hostile. 'That's for me to decide. I didn't ask for your interference, and I don't want it. I'm only interested in getting a good story, and to do that I need to try all the angles.'

Ryker's expression was distinctly unimpressed. 'Even to the extent of getting involved with the police?'

'I'm working,' she persisted. 'I have a job to do and I'll do whatever's necessary to get it done properly. There's no reason for you or anyone else to concern yourself with my affairs, and I'll thank you to leave me alone.' She jerked away from him, moving towards the window, the T-shirt sliding errantly down to expose the creamy smooth slope of her shoulder. Ryker's stare seared into her, burning on to her skin.

'You know me better than that, Cassie. I came to take you out of here, and I don't intend to leave empty-handed.'

'Ah, of course, there we have it,' she said, viewing him with disdain. 'I was forgetting your army roots—a mercenary, were you? I hadn't thought of offering you cash.' She began a fruitless search in the pockets of her jeans. 'Nothing there, I'm afraid. Maybe we could have a whip-round.'

His eyes hardened. 'You're pushing your luck,' he growled.

'Am I?' she seethed. 'If I was just anybody, I could do as I pleased without anyone batting an eyelid.'

He seemed to find that amusing. 'If you were just anybody,' he agreed, 'you could dance naked in the street, and damn the consequences. But you're not. You're the daughter of a very wealthy and powerful man, and getting involved in bad publicity does neither of you any good.'

'These people have every right to have their case brought out in the open,' she argued hotly. 'It isn't their fault they have nowhere to stay, and it's criminal that places like this old house stand empty for years on end while there are people in desperate need. It's time someone stood up for their rights.'

'Pity the poor students, is that it?'

'Too right,' she said with vehemence. 'They're not paid enough to live on—how are they supposed to manage on a mere pittance?'

'And are you setting yourself up as their leading light, campaigning for their cause?' His glance was filled with scepticism, and her spine stiffened.

'How does anything ever get done if no one wants to stand up and be counted?' she threw back.

'Very commendable, Cassie, but you can't take on every lame duck you come across.'

She released her breath in a short burst of exasperation. What was the point in even trying to explain anything to him? 'You don't understand.'

'I understand perfectly,' he said drily. 'You enjoy it, don't you? You thrive on trouble. You and Driscoll both. I heard he'd joined the team at the *Despatch*. What brought that on? Couldn't he keep away from you? Still drooling at your heels, is he?'

'It was a job opportunity that came his way,' she said stiffly. 'It was the paper that influenced his decision, not my presence.'

Ryker was scornful. 'That rag?'

'It's a perfectly sound paper,' she retorted.

His mouth made a dissentient twist. 'Driscoll doesn't exactly add to its integrity with his prying lens.' He sent another glance around the room. 'He's the least of my concerns, though. We have to get you away from here before the police arrive. I suggest you make a start on collecting together your belongings.'

She stood her ground. 'I am not leaving here; I thought I had made that quite clear.'

'I think you may find you want to change your mind after I've talked to the others.'

It was her turn to be scornful. 'What can you possibly say to them that will in any way change the situation?'

'Perhaps you overlook the fact that I have a few friends in the land-development business? One in particular has come up with an arrangement that will most probably suit everyone . . . an offer of accommodation for all concerned, within reach of the college, and at a rental they can all afford—provided they leave here this evening. Any confrontation with the police, and the offer will be withdrawn immediately. They'd be fools to turn it down, don't you agree?'

She drew in a long breath. She might have known that he would have everything sewn up, all the angles tied. That was the way he worked.

He moved away from her, walking out of the room, and she stared after him, trying to make sense of the seething tide of her emotions. She was bewildered by the surge of feeling he provoked in her whenever he was near, by the isolation she felt when he had gone, the blank emptiness that was left in his wake. He would never know the true intensity of her feelings for him. She could never reveal the way she felt and risk his embarrassed reaction. He had always been affectionate towards her, caring, considerate—because she was her father's daughter, the daughter of the man who had encouraged him in the early stages of his air-charter business.

Her career was what she should be concentrating all her energy on, not empty dreams of love that could never be fulfilled. Ryker was here for one reason: to take her away from the squat, and impending trouble. His presence here threatened to undermine all the work she had put in over these last few weeks.

How could she stop him? There was no way she could win once he had put his proposition to the others. Of course they wouldn't turn away a chance like that. They were being handed the golden key on a platter, weren't they? It was the answer to all their problems.

She frowned thoughtfully. Maybe it wasn't all lost. There was another slant she could try. An interview with this influential friend wouldn't go amiss some time, if she could fix it up.

Nick broke in on her preoccupation. Shorter than Ryker by three or four inches, he had the lithe frame of a man used to activity. 'What's happening?' He adjusted the strap on his camera, sliding it over his shoulder. 'Do we still have a story?'

Briefly she recounted what Ryker had said, and Nick's grey eyes narrowed. 'It's a pity we can't keep the police angle, but never mind,' he mused. 'There's still a chance I can get some good pictures, even now.' He flicked back the waving brown hair that persisted in falling down over his forehead.

'I'm not sure that's a good idea,' Cassie said. 'You know Ryker doesn't like to be involved in that kind of publicity. You could be stirring up a hornets' nest. Leave it; we can use what you already have.'

He went back downstairs, leaving Cassie to search for her holdall, and a few minutes later Ryker came back into the room. 'That's all settled, then,' he said with obvious satisfaction. 'Are you packed and ready to go?' He looked around expectantly.

'Stop gloating,' Cassie said. 'You knew you couldn't lose, you smooth-talking——'

'Language, Cassandra,' he admonished her softly. 'If you can't bring yourself to thank me for helping out, try at least to remember you're a lady.'

'*Thank* you?' she echoed tersely. 'Did you seriously expect me to thank you for what you did?' She shook her head at his folly. 'Don't hold your breath, will you? What you've done is simply to succeed in burying the problem where no one can see it for what it is. You've provided nothing more than a temporary salve to pour over the wound. What we need is publicity to get the powers that be to take notice and do something for people everywhere. It isn't enough that just a handful are fortunate enough to benefit from someone's afterdinner *bonhomie*. We need wide-scale action and results.'

'Right now, all I'm concerned about is keeping you out of the hands of the police, and out of court.' His glance shifted over the holdall. 'Is that it, then? Are you ready at last? I didn't see your car outside—I take it you still have the old Ford?'

She gave a brief nod of assent. 'I wouldn't dream of parting with it.'

He grimaced. 'Don't tell me it's at the garage again? As I recall, you always did put too much faith in it.'

Her frosty silence told him all he wanted to know, and his mouth quirked. 'I might have guessed. In that case, you can come with me. I'll give you a lift back to your flat.'

With sharp, angry movements, Cassie pushed the last of her things into the bag, and zipped it shut. Straightening, she said curtly, 'I hardly think there would be much point in doing that, since you've just effectively rendered me homeless.'

'Homeless?' he echoed, but she ignored his puzzled query, taking the stairs swiftly, her tread light and energetic. Ryker kept much too close for comfort. Reaching the hall, she watched the others troop out into the street through what was left of the door he had shattered.

'I don't follow,' he said, attempting to take the bag as they went out into the warmth of the early evening. 'Your father gave me your new address.'

Resisting, Cassie moved jerkily, and the ricochet of the loaded bag hit him in the calves.

He made a grab for her waist as she tried to walk away. 'Just stop and explain yourself,' he ordered, pulling her around to face him. His touch unnerved her, a feverish, unbidden heat racing like wildfire along her veins, and she stumbled against the hard length of him, the holdall slipping from her fingers. His lean, muscled body acted as a buffer for the softness of her curves, and the colour rose swiftly to her cheeks. Dazed, she was caught unawares by a sudden flashing light that blinded her temporarily, and she turned her head in time to see Nick disappearing down the avenue, checking his camera as he went.

He must have decided to get one last shot of the building. It was unfortunate that he had taken it just as she and Ryker emerged.

'One of these days,' Ryker said grittily, 'that man is going to answer to me. What do you mean, you're homeless?'

He was completely unaffected by their brief closeness. Cassie shifted away from the confining hold of his strong hands, and made an effort to bring her breathing under control. 'The builders are working on my flat just at the moment,' she told him. 'I've never been fond of brick dust.'

He was unperturbed. 'Then I'll take you to your father's house,' he offered.

'You certainly will not,' she bit out. 'I am not going to Bourton Manor. What gives you the idea that I can take off for the North Downs at a moment's notice? It's much too far away. I've a story to get out, or had you forgotten? Perhaps you thought you'd done enough damage to make me drop the whole idea—well, you're wrong. You may have put a blight on it, but there must be something I can salvage. I'll get a room somewhere.'

'You never give up, do you?' he said tersely. 'I suppose it was you who put Driscoll up to that photo stunt—anything for publicity.'

'I fail to see why you should assume that,' she retorted, hurt that he should think that way. 'And anyway, it's hardly unexpected if Nick uses his camera at every opportunity. It's what he's paid to do, after all—and you are newsworthy. It's the price you pay for shooting to the top in the world of high-powered business. If you don't like it, you'll simply have to resort to dark glasses and a Homburg pulled down low over your brow.' She started to walk away, but he was too quick for her.

'Not so fast.' His hand snaked out and tethered her wrist. 'I said I'd give you a lift, and I meant it.'

His car was parked alongside the pavement, a sleek sports model, built for speed. 'Get in,' he said, his mouth hard. He jerked open the passenger door and she looked at his chiselled expression and thought twice about giving him any argument for the moment. Moodily, she slid into the leather-covered seat.

'I suppose I'd better try the King's Arms first,' she muttered. 'They usually have a room available, and they're not too expensive.'

He started up the engine, and she watched his hands move on the wheel, firm and in control. He was a good driver, she had acknowledged that long ago, and after a while she leaned back, his smooth handling of the power-packed car lulling her into a brooding silence. They were headed outwards, through the busy London streets, leaving the crowded inner city behind them, and it was only as they passed by the King's Arms and kept on going that she said stiffly, 'What are you doing? I've told you where I want to go. Turn the car around.'

'A hotel doesn't strike me as a good idea. A woman alone at night in the city might be prey to all kinds of danger.'

'Aren't you taking a lot on yourself?' she remarked coldly. 'I prefer to make my own decisions. Take me back.'

'I think not, Cassandra. My place strikes me as a much better idea.'

CHAPTER TWO

CASSIE sucked in her breath. The very idea of staying with Ryker, of being in such close proximity to him for any length of time, had her nerves jumping erratically in feverish disarray, her pulse beating out a rapid tattoo. She mustn't let this happen. Over the last few years she had gone out of her way to have only the minimum contact with him, and she couldn't let him shatter her peace of mind now. Ryker at a distance she could just about cope with; Ryker by her side put altogether too much of a strain on her defences.

'I already told you,' she said with taut emphasis, 'I've no intention of going to the North Downs.'

'No, I wasn't referring to the house; I've an apartment in London now, too. I find it's convenient when I'm here on business.'

'Really? Well, I have no wish to stay with you, Ryker, and I'll thank you to stop this car and let me out. I'll take a taxi. At least cab drivers do as they're bid.'

He glanced at her obliquely. 'I fail to see quite what you're so het up about, Cassandra,' he murmured drily. 'I wasn't suggesting we set up house together, merely that I put you up for a night or two.'

He was laughing at her. Did he know what she was feeling, how much his presence disturbed her? Surely he could not? At any rate, she meant to keep a tight rein on her physical reactions to him, and she resented his calm dismissiveness.

'You're too fond of having things your own way,' she retorted. 'You seem to think you can do just as you please, regardless of my feelings.'

'Nonsense. Anyway, we're here now.'

They were in a secluded, tree-lined close, she saw, where the distinctive red-brick buildings all had a certain quiet elegance, fronted by gleaming wrought iron and steps leading to the ground floor.

'We overlook the park,' he said. 'I like it here, especially at this time of year.'

If he was trying to woo her into acquiescence, he wasn't going to succeed, she thought churlishly. Her mouth set in a firm line. Getting out of the car, she walked purposefully towards the boot, ready to grab her bag and go, but he had already lifted out her holdall and was striding up the steps to the imposing mahogany door.

'Ryker,' she mouthed sharply, 'you're an interfering——'

'Save it,' he said briskly. 'It's late, and we've both had a long day.'

He disappeared into the hall with her belongings, and mounted the stairs to his second-floor apartment. She followed with ill concealed rancour.

The lounge was long, and wide, furnished in the cool and uncluttered manner of a man who liked space and stylish simplicity.

'I never met a more stubborn, mulish man,' she said bitingly, going after him as he went through to the kitchen. 'First you barge in and totally destroy the article I'm working on, and now you have the utter gall to whisk me away and deposit me here without so much as a by-your-leave. It wouldn't occur to you that I prefer to be within shouting distance of my editor, would it? No, you have to come along like a raging buccaneer and snatch me away.'

'I thought you were planning on salvaging the article,' he commented, spooning coffee into a percolator, and setting the switch.

She glowered at him, and he said with needling provocation, 'I really can't see why you're making such a fuss. Am I dragging you away from Driscoll, is that the problem?' His eyes narrowed, coldly penetrating. 'It wouldn't be the first time.'

He turned away from her, picking up her holdall and taking it from the room, and she watched him go, fighting against the angry colour that stole into her cheeks. He had done it deliberately, brought up that dreadful, humiliating incident just to crush her. How could he bring up something that had happened five years ago? That day was all too deeply imprinted on her memory, wasn't it? She hadn't needed his barbed reminder.

Nothing had gone right that afternoon, she recalled. Nick had been staying at Bourton Manor for a few days. He'd been there to write up a feature on her father, and he was taking photos of their home, and the well tended estate.

'How did you get started in the newspaper business?' she'd asked urgently. 'Did you work your way up from the bottom, or did you do a course first and then apply around?' His work had fascinated her. It had been her own dream to do something like that. 'Which interests you the most—the writing, or the photography?'

Nick had laughed at her questions, shot at him rapid-fire, so keen had she been to know everything, and he'd done his best to answer. Perhaps he had been flattered by her attention.

But that particular afternoon, five years ago, she'd been thankful he was not around. The arguments between her and her father were nothing new, but she did not want her new-found friend to witness them.

James Wyatt had set ideas on what she should make of her life. Her career was mapped out—by him, on his terms—and it seemed that her wishes had no place in his decision-making.

At seventeen, she fiercely resented his attempts to mould her will to his own, and this time the bitter aftermath of their furious clash hung like a pall over the house, filling her with an overwhelming need to escape.

She was not thinking clearly when she ran from the house. Nick, returning from his trip to town, almost collided with her, but she rushed past him. All that was in her head was the beckoning tranquillity of the lake, the lush green of the grass where she could throw herself down and hide from the world behind the rambling hedgerow. Nick followed, though, curious about her sudden flight.

'What's wrong, Cassie?' he asked, questioning the slow trickle of tears she fought to hold back. 'Tell me.'

She was terribly vulnerable just then, needing the comfort of another person, and Nick was there to listen and soothe, and pour balm on her fractured soul. Perhaps that was why, after the first few wary moments, she allowed herself to be folded into his embrace.

'It's my father,' she told him haltingly. 'He's determined that I shall join the family business.' Nick smoothed back the damp tendrils of her hair, and she sniffed and said, 'It isn't what I want. He should have had a son to carry on the tradition. I can't do it. I want to write—why can't he understand that?'

'He wants you to stay in the family home,' Nick said. 'Is that so unnatural? You're going to be very wealthy one day, an heiress—isn't there a trust fund, some kind of settlement from your grandparents? Shouldn't you go along with his wishes, rather than alienate him?'

She was taken aback a little by his knowledge of their family affairs. How did he know all that? It wasn't like her father to reveal so much to someone he had only just begun to know.

'I can't do as he wants,' she muttered. 'I'll be a cipher, nothing more.'

'But a rich one,' Nick murmured. 'Isn't that worth keeping the boat steady for the next few years at least?'

Miserably, she shook her head, and he studied her thoughtfully for a moment. Then, taking her face in his hands, he kissed her gently, with slow deliberation. She was not sure she liked that kiss, but the hand stroking her hair was soothing, and she gradually succumbed to his caresses. His advances soon became increasingly passionate, and she floundered, youth and inexperience adding to her uncertainty.

Confused and unhappy, her reactions were like those of someone waking from a bad dream. Slowly her thoughts began to coalesce into a recognisable whole. She did not want this. Belatedly, she tried to call a halt, her palms pushing against his chest in futile restraint.

'Please, Nick, I——'

'It's all right, Cassie, believe me...'

The sound of bracken crackling underfoot brought her into startled awareness of their surroundings. She looked up, and saw Ryker looming over them, his features dark and forbidding, and her stomach turned a somersault.

'Am I interrupting something?' he enquired, his tone caustic, the glitter of his eyes harsh as they swept over her dishevelled state.

Mortified, Cassie tried to pull together the edges of her blouse, tremblingly conscious of his contemptuous gaze firing along the creamy slope of her breasts. Her cheeks burned. Why did he have to find her like this?

Nick stood up. 'I'd have thought,' he said with rash belligerence, 'that it was fairly obvious your company is not wanted.'

'Isn't that too bad?' Ryker gritted, deep sarcasm crusting his words. 'This happens to be my land, and I'd prefer you do your lovemaking elsewhere.'

'Your land?' Nick repeated, plainly taken aback.

'You heard what I said,' Ryker told him forcefully. 'See to it that you leave—now, unless you want me to lay on a charge of trespass.' The grim menace of his expression left no doubt that he would take the law into his own hands if necessary.

Turning his attention back to Cassie, his lancing scrutiny ripped through the already lacerated edges of her composure. She put up a hand to her hot face. As Nick began to move away, she struggled to her feet, the folds of her cotton skirt hampering her as she made to go after him.

Ryker caught her arm. 'Not you, Cassie,' he commanded. His fingers were like a band of iron around her flesh as he pulled her towards him, and she was fiercely, vibrantly aware of his strength, his powerful masculinity. 'Haven't you any more sense than to get involved with him?' he gritted harshly.

Her mind refused to work. He was devastatingly close, his touch firing her into tingling awareness. She blinked, her limbs dissolving in shocked recognition of what was happening to her. This was why she had felt nothing when Nick held her. It was Ryker, and Ryker alone, who dominated her being, scored a path through her heart.

He stared down at her, and she was stunned by the anger that burned fathoms deep in his eyes. Anger, and something else. Something she did not recognise.

'Ryker,' she began shakily, trembling as the fingers of her free hand brushed against his chest. She felt him stiffen. 'I didn't mean——'

He pushed her away. It was as though the sound of her voice had slammed down a shutter within him. 'Tidy yourself up,' he said brutally, his mouth a hard, grim line. 'Your father's on his way over here.'

'My father?' The anguished acknowledgement of her new discovery clouded her concentration. 'What—what do you mean?'

'I've already said. He's on his way over here. We have a meeting in...' he checked his watch '...five minutes.' His eyes seared her. 'Unless you want your father to see you looking as though you've just been bedded, I suggest you do something about your blouse.'

Shame coursed through her veins as she looked down at her rumpled clothing and saw herself through his eyes. Shakily, she dealt with the last of her buttons. When she had finished, she looked up and found him studying her flushed features with a dark, savage intensity that made her flinch. She had never seen him so angry, so distant.

He said tersely, 'You'd better hope he doesn't take the lakeside path. It would take more than a few minutes to wipe away that look of wanton sensuality.'

Her heart gave a painful lurch. It's you, she cried inwardly. You're the reason . . .

He looked at her, cynicism etched into his hard mouth. 'What are you, Cassandra? Half child, half woman—a volatile, dangerous combination, far too dangerous to be running wild where the Driscolls of this world are concerned. I doubt very much that you can handle the consequences you reap.'

It was her feelings for him that she had never been able to handle. There was nothing childlike in her emotional response to him, nor in the way she craved his recognition of her growing love. But Ryker was never short of female attention; she had learned that very early on. Women were drawn to him like moths to the flame, and those who he chose to date all had one thing in common—they were nothing like Cassie. They were sophisticated, glamorous, wordly wise.

Even now, that knowledge had the power to cut deep. Pushing back the painful memories, Cassie sat down at the table and stared around the kitchen, the blip blip of the percolator barely encroaching on her consciousness. Ryker walked into the room and switched it off, pouring the hot liquid into two ceramic mugs.

'Daydreaming?' he enquired abrasively, and she stared at him with bitter dislike.

'I was seventeen,' she said. 'I needed your interference then as little as I need it now.'

He pushed a steaming mug across the table towards her. 'You took a risk, getting involved with him, knowing he was only in the area to do a photo feature on your father. I expect he could have made a killing on the information you sent his way. But no doubt the beguiling charms of the daughter persuaded him to be more circumspect than his usual manner.'

'Your view of things is completely warped,' she told him icily.

'Is it? He may have adhered to the rules with your father, but he's had no such scruples in the articles he's produced on me since then, has he?' He stared at her hard, his features taut. 'From the amount of detail he puts in, I think I might be forgiven for wondering just how he comes by that information.'

His words stung. What detail did he mean? His home, his background? Did he really think she would have given Nick anything that could be slanted against him? Anyway, she did not know for sure any of the intimate goings-on in his life. There was only what she read in the Press, and she shied away from those reports. She hoped they were only guesswork, nothing more.

'He didn't need me to tell him about your conquests,' she said tightly. 'It seems to be common knowledge that women are only too eager to throw themselves into your net like suicidal butterflies.' She sipped at her coffee.

Ryker smiled drily. 'Been reading your own paper, have you?'

She put down her mug with a faint snap, and got to her feet, scraping back her chair. 'Thanks for reminding me. As you said, it's late, and I have work to finish off. My editor expects an article of some sort to arrive on his desk, whether or not there's been outside interference. If you'll excuse me,' she said with exaggerated politeness, 'I'll go to my room.' She walked to a door which led off from the kitchen. 'Is it through here?'

His mouth slanted attractively. 'By all means,' he murmured. 'It does happen to be my room, but if you insist on sharing I shan't put any objections in the way.'

Amusement danced in his gleaming amber gaze, and she clenched her fingers into fists at her sides. He was making fun of her, tormenting her at every opportunity. 'Don't flatter yourself, Ryker,' she gritted.

There was only one other door, and she went through it, relieved to find herself in a small guest bedroom. Slamming the door shut, she drove the bolt home, her temperature rising like quicksilver as she heard Ryker's soft chuckle on the other side.

Sleep did nothing to improve her temper. Ryker had taken a perverse delight in annoying her, and she had been foolish enough to leave herself wide open to his devilish baiting. She found it hard to forgive herself that lapse.

Ever since he had arrived at the squat, he had played havoc with her concentration, and she could not let that state of affairs continue. As soon as she had showered, she would phone the office. Her work had been disrupted long enough.

On second thoughts, she'd do it now. There was always someone on hand at the office to take copy,

however early, and with any luck Ryker would still
be asleep. She might even be able to leave him a
note and slip away without encountering him again.
He was obviously going to take any chance he could
to provoke her, and she would simply not allow
him the pleasure any longer.

Rummaging through her bag, she lifted out her
silk robe and pulled it on over her underwear, tying
the belt firmly at her waist before she went through
to the kitchen.

Ryker, though, was standing by the window as
she walked into the room, a coffee-cup in his hand
as he looked out over the park. Her step faltered.
He was wearing casual clothes, as on the previous
day, but the cut of his beige trousers was
undeniably expensive, moulding strong thighs and
fitting smoothly over his lean torso. Her glance
flickered away distractedly.

He turned around fully then, viewing her over
the rim of his cup before he drained the last of his
coffee. His shirt collar was open, revealing the
deeply bronzed column of his throat.

'Good morning,' he murmured, replacing his cup
on the sill. His lambent gaze shifted slowly over her
slender shape, pausing to linger on the rounded
curve of hip and thigh outlined by the clinging folds
of material. She was tautly conscious of the scant
state of her dress, but she gave him a quelling stare,
resentfully remembering his teasing remark of the
previous night.

Undaunted, his wandering glance slid down to
take in the long, smooth line of her legs, the fine,

sloping arch of her bare feet. He was doing it deliberately, in order to goad her, she decided, bitterly aware of the treacherous nature of her own body as her skin warmed in response to his scorching appraisal.

'I hadn't expected to find you up yet,' she said abruptly, her mood fractious. From the appetising smell of fritters and eggs that assaulted her nostrils, she gathered he must already have breakfasted.

'I have a business to run,' he commented with laconic ease. 'Did you sleep well?'

'Well enough.'

Her tone was grouchy, and his mouth slanted in amusement. 'Not a morning person, are you, Cassie?'

Her fingers toyed with the sash of her robe. Why did he have this effect on her? Surely she had outgrown the foolish infatuation that had rendered her helpless in the past? She could see clearly now, and she would not let herself fall under his spell. Being close to Ryker was like being suspended fast within a force field; his attraction was a potent and dangerous thing. This time, though, she would not be caught by it. She was determined. It was not fair, she reasoned. When he chose to, he could charm the birds off the trees, but she would never set herself up as a source for his amusement.

'There's coffee, and more fritters in the pan,' he said, going over to the table and applying butter liberally to a crusty roll.

He had an appetite like a warrior, she thought restively, watching him eat. Yet there was not an

ounce of spare flesh on him. He burned up energy
too fast; he was all hard muscle, fit and vigorous,
his body toned like an athlete's.

'Is something wrong?' he enquired pleasantly, his
hands momentarily stilled, and she realised with a
shock that she must have been staring.

Her blue eyes skittered away. Stiff-lipped, she
asked, 'May I use your phone?'

He inclined his head in the direction of the
lounge. 'Help yourself.'

Going through to the other room, she sat cross-
legged on the couch and dialled her office, relating
her story to the typist on the receiving end. Having
dealt with that task to her satisfaction, she was just
about to ring off when Jim Harker's irascible tones
came on the line. She steeled herself for a dressing
down. Her boss was never in the best of moods
first thing.

'If you're not at the squat,' he said tightly, 'where
are you calling from?'

She told him, and there was a momentary pause.
Then, 'Ryker Haldene, did you say?' His voice took
on a note of suppressed excitement. 'Now there's
a touch of good fortune. You realise he's taking
part in the air show next week, don't you? All the
proceeds are to go to various charities, so it was a
real feather in their cap for the organisers to get
him to agree to make an appearance. Now that's a
story that will really pull our readers in. They'll be
gasping to know what makes him tick. Go for it,
girl; you're on the spot. I'll expect to hear
from you——'

'But you don't understand . . .' Cassie tried to get a word in. 'He doesn't—I can't——'

'You're babbling, Cassandra. Quit stalling and get on with it. You've a heaven-sent opportunity there; it's been handed to you on a plate. Another thing—I heard he might be paying a visit to one of his pursuits centres in a few weeks; he doesn't do that very often. They were something he set up before he went into the air-charter business, so it could be a new angle for us. Go along with him and see what mileage you can get out of it.'

'But I can't do that. He doesn't like the articles the *Despatch* put out—and can you blame him? If you didn't keep changing everything, giving them a different slant, it might be a different matter. It's not on, Jim; I'm not submitting any articles on him if you plan to mess them about.'

'You worry too much,' he said dismissively. 'We're here to sell papers, not nurse sensibilities. Just get on with the job, Cassandra. I need journalists who bring in the goods. Remember that.'

'Jim, it isn't——'

She was talking to the air. In his usual precipitate manner, he had already cut the call.

She glowered in angry frustration at the buzzing receiver for a moment, before slapping it back on to its base.

'Trouble?' Ryker appeared in front of her, one dark brow lifting in query.

He had startled her out of her preoccupation, and she jumped, her senses thrown into confusion by his unexpected approach.

'I—er—no.'

She frowned, and tried to pull herself together, viewing him in an abstracted fashion. Any hope she might have entertained of slipping quietly away and removing herself from the perilous mouth of the tiger's lair had just flown straight out of the window, hadn't it?

If she valued her job, she was going to have to work with him now, somehow persuade him into letting her write a piece on him, and at the same time prevent Jim Harker from tampering with it. It was stretching the bounds of possibility to hope that Ryker might agree. Any other paper, perhaps. Any other journalist... She ran a hand through her hair. Lord, what a mess.

Ryker's stare was quizzical. 'No?' he repeated. 'Are you sure? From the look on your face, anyone might think you've just been landed with an outsize problem.'

Choking slightly, she averted her head, turning her pained reaction into a cough. Problem? What problem? she derided herself inwardly. It was nothing she couldn't handle, was it, given a few months to prepare the ground?

CHAPTER THREE

'DIDN'T you say something about breakfast?' Cassie said brightly. Springing up from the sofa, she headed towards the kitchen. 'Shall I make more coffee?'

A dart of challenge flashed in the depths of his eyes. 'Deflective tactics? That was your editor you were talking to, I assume. Is everything OK?'

'Fine, fine,' she lied. 'What could possibly be wrong?'

'What indeed?' he echoed softly.

She avoided his narrowed gaze. Lifting the lid on a pan, she scooped out a couple of potato fritters and slid them on to a plate, taking them over to the table. When she was seated, she took time to glance around. 'Nice place you have here,' she murmured between mouthfuls. 'Have you had it long?'

To her relief, he accepted the change of subject without further comment. 'A few months. My visits to the capital are more frequent these days.'

'You're no stranger on the international circuit, either,' she said with a wry inflexion. 'Your air-charter business didn't just bloom, it proliferated beyond all imagining, didn't it? I guessed it would happen years ago; you were never one to let time lie idle on your hands.'

'I could say the same thing about you. You haven't exactly stayed still over the last few years, have you? University, a bright career just beginning to take off, a new home. Do you ever miss being at Bourton Manor?'

'Not at all. My place may be small, and a lot needs doing to it, but at least it's all my own, and I have my independence. There's a lot to be said for being a free agent.'

Finishing off the last of the food, she leaned back in her chair, and breathed deeply, lazily crossing one leg over the other. His gaze tracked the indolent, sensuous movement.

'That was good,' she said. 'Sheer delight, a feast of indulgence.' She linked her hands behind her head, sending the tumbled dark waves that massed around her shoulders into a flurry of disorder. 'I shall have to let you cook for me again some time.'

'Hmm.' He assessed her narrowly. 'In the meantime, maybe you had better get dressed. I have work to do.'

Her mouth made a moue of discontent, its message dissolved by the faint sparkle in her eyes. 'And I'd been hoping you might spare me some time—just a few moments—to listen to a small proposition I have to put to you.'

'I knew something was hatching in that devious brain. If it involves your newspaper, you can forget it.'

'Me? Devious? How could you think such a thing?' She sent him an affronted look.

Whatever he might have been about to reply was swallowed up in the sudden clatter made by the opening and closing of an outer door. The sound of footsteps in the hall followed.

Cassie threw him a swift glance, but he did not seem at all concerned by the intrusion.

'That will be Sophie,' he said. 'I asked her to stop by.'

The unexpected entrance of Sophie Tremayne still managed to throw Cassie a little off balance. Ryker's secretary was no stranger to her, and she was, as usual, a model of sophistication that put Cassie's own casual attire to shame. The smooth blonde chignon was immaculate, the cream linen suit cut in classic lines that made the most of her shapely figure, her well shaped feet encased in stylish leather shoes with three-inch heels.

Sophie's cold blue glance wafted over Cassie like a draught of Arctic wind. There had never, Cassie reflected ruefully, been any love lost between her and Sophie. Even though, on several occasions, she had attempted to break the ice, the barrier always remained steadfastly intact.

Turning to Ryker, Sophie said, 'I saw your car outside, so I guessed you were at home—though I hadn't realised Cassandra would be with you. I hope you didn't mind my using the key, but obviously you didn't hear my knock.'

She held out a manila file towards him. 'The notes you asked for,' she remarked. 'I think you'll find everything's in order.'

'Thanks.' Ryker took it from her, opening it up and riffling through the papers. 'That was quick work.'

She gave him a knock-out smile. 'I believe you said it was fairly urgent.'

'It is.' He weighed the package in his hand. 'Help yourself to coffee while I go and deal with this. I'm sure you and Cassie will have plenty to talk about.'

Sometimes, Cassie thought disgustedly, men could be so blind. Was he really unaware of the antipathy that existed between the two women? Sophie was older than she was by six years, and perhaps that was the reason they could find no common ground. And, of course, Sophie had been in Ryker's employ from the very beginning. Her place in his life was well established.

The door closed behind Ryker, and Sophie turned a cool gaze on Cassie. 'I suppose I should have guessed you would be here. Ryker said you were involved in some kind of scrape. It really is too much, you know. He has far more important things to do than spend time sorting you out.'

Cassie lifted a negligent shoulder. 'Am I stopping him? I didn't ask to come here.'

Sophie's mouth tightened. 'You know, you really ought to realise by now that there's no future for you with Ryker.'

Cassie raised a finely arched brow in query and Sophie smiled thinly. 'It was always perfectly obvious to me how you feel about him. But you're wasting your time.' She flicked a speck of wool from her skirt with long, manicured fingernails. 'The

only reason that he bothers with you at all is because his integrity is deeply ingrained. He values
the friendship he has with your father, and he'd
hate to see you do anything that will cause James
any adverse publicity.'

'You profess to know an awful lot about the way
Ryker thinks,' Cassie remarked coolly. 'Since when
did you have a through-line to his psyche?'

Sophie's tone was laced with scorn. 'Ryker and
I have worked together since he moved next to
Bourton Manor, had you forgotten? Don't you
think that was bound to make us close?'

How could Cassie ever doubt it?

'Of course,' Sophie went on, 'we've both been
far too busy following our careers to take the final
step, but it's only a matter of time. At the moment,
he's too much involved with other commitments,
travelling the world over, but he wouldn't dream
of leaving me behind.' She paused, smiling faintly.
'So you see, Cassandra, if you're hoping that your
infatuation can come to something, you're hoping
in vain.'

'Aren't you making a lot of assumptions?' Cassie
put in sharply. 'Why on earth should you have the
idea that I harbour any emotions at all where Ryker
is concerned?'

Sophie laughed. 'Oh, come on, give me some
credit. I'm a woman; I can see these things. But
you really don't have a chance, you know. Ryker
needs a woman who can smooth his path, make
sure that the wheels of his life are well oiled.'

Her cold gaze skimmed over Cassie's *déshabillé*, the riotous tumble of ebony hair, the bare feet. 'Why would he look twice at you? You don't even dress the part. I'll bet you still spend all your time in jeans and T-shirts.' Her lips thinned. 'Take it from me, he might amuse himself with you for a time, but that's all it is—a temporary distraction.'

'I'm so glad you told me,' Cassie said with tight sarcasm. 'I might not have slept nights, thinking that I filled his every waking thought.'

Ryker came back into the kitchen, and she stood up, muttering tersely, 'I'm going to take a shower.'

Gathering up her clothes on the way, she headed for the bathroom, locking the door behind her.

Was there any truth in what Sophie had said? She turned the shower full on, honing it to a fierce jet. Steam filled the room. How close was his relationship with his secretary? And was it possible he might suspect how Cassie herself felt about him? Just the thought of the humiliation that would bring brought a flush of heat to her face.

It was true, she acknowledged unhappily, stepping under the sharp spray; right from the start, when he had first arrived at her father's house for a business meeting, she had been knocked for six by his powerful male presence. When he'd bought the neighbouring property, his appearances around the place had soon become the centre of her universe. The mere sound of his voice had been enough to set her pulse racing, the blood pounding her body with frantic haste.

He was ruggedly masculine, and she had been overwhelmingly attracted to him; there was no denying it. But Sophie was always there, in the background, and it was clear that a man like Ryker could have his pick of women. What chance had a naïve young girl had of gaining any prominent place in his life? He liked her, though; she knew that. From the beginning they had shared an easy friendship, and he had never objected to her wandering freely over his land. The small copse and the lake had always been her bolt-hole in times of stress, the place she retreated to when the arguments with her father became too much to bear.

She did not remember her mother, and she often wondered if things might have been easier if she had lived, if a woman's touch might have softened her father. He did not understand her. His temper, always notoriously uncertain, had plumbed new depths that summer, when she was seventeen. Unwittingly passing by the study as he'd emerged with Ryker, Cassie had caught the brunt of it.

'Where are you going?' her father grated. 'I want to talk to you. I've just received the prospectus for the business and economics course at the university and I want to go through it with you before I leave for Switzerland.' He scanned her skimpy ribbed top and her bare midriff with taut censure.

Cassie's blue eyes darkened, an ominous glitter smouldering in their depths. He thought he could intimidate her with his harsh manner, but he would not succeed.

'We've talked about this before,' she reminded him evenly, 'and you know perfectly well that I don't want to take that kind of course. I'm sorry; I've tried to take an interest in the company, but land development doesn't hold out the remotest enticement for me. Uprooting people from their homes so that an office block or a shopping complex can go in their place goes against the grain. There are other things I plan to do with my life.'

'Writing, you mean?' Disapproval edged his voice. 'Just because you've managed to put out a few short stories doesn't mean that you have any major talent for it, and I'm certainly not funding you to spend the next three or four years doodling. You can think again.'

'I've already thought it through,' Cassie said firmly, her shoulders stiff with determination. 'I'm going to study journalism, and I'll pay for it myself out of the money my grandmother left me.'

James Wyatt let out an explosive hiss. He had never enjoyed being thwarted. 'I've no time to waste on this; I have arrangements to make for my trip.' He turned to Ryker. 'Can't you talk to her? She listens to you. See if you can't get her to see sense.'

Ryker studied her thoughtfully, and her fingers twisted in agitation. She rammed her hands into the pockets of her shorts. 'My mind is made up,' she said, 'and besides, I have things to do right now.'

She left the house with the sound of her father's anger rumbling in the background, and set off along the road for the village shop. Her father had never tried to understand her point of view and these arguments always left her taut with mounting frustration. Her own temper was rapidly coming to the boil, and she had to walk it off, or burst.

After half an hour, she began to wonder if there was not a better method of dealing with her warring emotions. The oppressive warmth of the afternoon did nothing to contain her anger. The sun beat down on her without mercy, aggravating her already frayed nerves. Her father was too full of himself, his own ideals, to have time to consider other people's opinions, let alone those of his daughter.

It did not take her long to purchase the few bits of stationery that she needed, and she made the return journey at a slower pace, flagging in the sweltering heat.

Without her realising it, her steps had taken her towards the lake, close to the rickety landing-stage that had long been in need of repair. With a sigh of relief, she sat down by the water's edge, watching the golden glow of the sun spread in a molten arc over its surface. The sky was a perfect, cloudless blue, the air hot, stifling, taking her breath away.

Restively, she looked around. The water looked invitingly cool, and no one was around to disturb her. Ryker usually swam in the morning, and his work occupied him for the major part of the day. Since the episode with Nick, she had kept out of his way as much as possible, not wanting to see a return of the harsh condemnation in his eyes. But he wasn't likely to be heading in this direction, was he? Why was she hesitating? Pulling off her top, she dropped it to one side, and stepped out of her shorts, standing in her flimsy underwear looking out over the calm water. The sun blazed down on her, a flaming orb, high in the sky, searing her flesh with its incandescent flame.

The lake whispered to her, and she moved towards it slowly, stepping into its welcoming embrace. For a long, breathtaking moment, she savoured its cool, silken touch on her burning skin. After a while, she turned on her back, making waves, revelling in the lap of water on her pliant body. Idly, she gave herself up to its enveloping arms, only turning her glance towards the distant grassy bank when she felt gloriously refreshed.

Instantly, the warmth was back, an uncomfortable ripple flowing unchecked through her veins. 'Ryker?' It shocked her to the core to see him standing by the water's edge, tall and lean, his amber gaze unerringly steady.

Hastily, she pushed herself upright, thankful that now at least only her shoulders were laid bare to his scrutiny. 'What are you doing here?'

'Shouldn't I be? It is my land, after all.'

She grimaced. 'I thought you would be working this afternoon—you don't usually come down to the lake at this time.'

Her glance flickered over his white trousers, the ice-blue shirt, unbuttoned at the neck. She closed her eyes for a brief moment, shutting out his image. He was far too attractive for her peace of mind.

'If you've come to argue with me about my father,' she muttered, 'I don't want to hear it.' Her hair clung damply about her face and shoulders, small rivulets trickling down to fall in glistening droplets on her skin.

He shrugged. 'Actually, I came to repair the landing-stage.'

Her brow furrowed, and slowly she scanned the bank, her gaze coming to rest at length on a canvas tool bag alongside some obviously new planking.

'Ah.' Warm colour suffused her cheeks. Of course he wouldn't be interested in sorting out her problems. He had other things to occupy his time. She cupped water in her palms and let it flow in a cooling stream over her gold-tinted arms. 'I suppose I'm in the way,' she said, perversely resenting his indifference. 'Are you planning on throwing me off as you threatened with Nick?'

His jaw tensed, the planes of his face darkly shuttered. 'I doubt that will be necessary.' His sardonic tone sparked a fiery edge along her already smarting sensibilities.

'I'm glad,' she muttered. 'It's really much too hot to get embroiled in a tussle.'

'True. It must rate as the hottest day this summer.' His brooding glance unnerved her, slanting as it did over the naked curve of her shoulders, coming to rest with unusual preoccupation on the tiny golden birthmark that lay on one smoothly rounded slope.

Suddenly, she found she had lost all desire to remain in the water. 'I'd like to come out of here,' she said. 'Turn around, would you? While I get dressed.'

His head went back slightly, as though his mind had been elsewhere and she had startled him with her words. He laughed softly, but did as she asked.

When she was fully clothed once more, she said coolly, 'Since you obviously have work to do, I'll get out of your way. I'd hate to bother you any longer than necessary.'

'Bother me?' he murmured. 'I'll let you know when that happens.'

He was right, of course. What made her think she could possibly disturb him in any way? He was a neighbour, a business associate of her father. He probably took her father's viewpoint, too.

'You won't solve any of your problems by scowling.' His amused tones penetrated the black cloud of her thoughts, and her gaze rested on him smokily. 'You should talk it through with him, calmly. Both of you let your tempers get the better of you, and then you walk away from the issue without hammering it out properly.'

'It's pointless. He doesn't understand any viewpoint but his own, and I'm through with trying to make him listen.'

'James is not used to dealing with rebellion. Your non-conformity irritates him.'

'My father and I will never agree.'

'That's true,' Ryker confirmed. 'You're too much alike. Without some give and take on either side, you'll neither of you get very far.'

'I can't reason with him,' she insisted. 'He has it stuck in his head that I'll join the firm, and nothing will shift that idea. My feelings are of no account to him.' Her lips moved in a faint twist of disillusion. 'He dismisses my opinions as if they have no bearing on anything. That's why we're always arguing. But I can't let him have his way on this. Writing is what I feel I can do best, and if he doesn't like it, well, that's too bad.' She tossed her head back lightly, and Ryker appraised her in silence, taking in the firm set of her mouth, the grim truculence in the taut angle of her jaw.

'Maybe he needs time to adjust,' he said. 'Lately he's been away more often than he's been at home. He has to learn how to cope with a daughter who's beginning to find her voice, a voice as strong as his own. It's taken him aback.'

Her blue eyes shifted with restless frustration. 'I can't see him trying to meet me halfway, can you? He may be my father, but there's no law that says we have to get on together.' She breathed in raggedly, the curve of her breasts slowly rising with the motion. 'Anyway, there's no need for you to involve yourself any further.' She swallowed, feeling strangely at odds with herself. 'You've done his bidding, haven't you? He asked you to talk to me, to point out the error of my ways. Well, consider it done. You can get on with other things now. You can do what you came here for.' Her voice wavered. 'Don't let me disturb you any longer.'

She made to turn away and he stopped her, his hands closing on her shoulders, drawing her around to face him.

'Wait, Cassie. There's no need to upset yourself. I'm sure it can all be sorted out in the end. You need to give it a little time. Allow things to calm down.'

'You take his side,' she muttered. 'Men always stick together. You all think women can be soothed with soft words, that you'll get your own way in the end.'

She started to pull away and he wound his arms around her, holding her close. 'No, sweetheart. It isn't that way at all.'

He was smiling down at her, his eyes warm and golden, his stare roaming over her sun-flushed face. And then everything seemed to change. There was a sudden stillness. The heat must be getting to her, she reasoned abstractedly; that was why she felt so dizzy, so out of control, why there was this peculiar weakness in the pit of her stomach.

His gaze drifted down to dwell on the full curve of her soft mouth, and her heartbeat jolted to a jerky, staccato rhythm. He moved closer, his head shading out the sun, and then he was taking her startled mouth with his own. His taste was warm and male, and there was a hint of musky fragrance faintly emanating from the pores of his skin. Her fingers collided helplessly with the hard-boned contours of his shoulders, slid along the smooth, muscled perfection of his chest as he eased her against his rugged frame.

A wild, unbidden quiver of longing shuddered through her. The kiss lingered, melting the nebulous shreds of her resistance in a sweetly flowing tide, a heady wash of intoxication that would not be stemmed. She was enthralled by him, drinking in the nectar she had craved so long.

When he finally drew his mouth from hers, she looked up at him, his features swimming hazily before her, as though the brilliance of the sun had invaded her being and blinded her to everything but him. He stared at her without speaking. His thumb trailed lightly over the throbbing fullness of her lips, his glance absorbing the hectic glitter of her eyes, the warm flushed pink of her cheeks.

'You're very sweet, Cassie,' he murmured. 'Very young, and delightfully responsive. But I think you had better go.' He pushed her away from him, holding her at arm's length. 'As you said, I have work to do, and Sophie will be arriving at the house in a couple of hours. We have a dinner date.'

'D-dinner?' She stumbled over the word, needing to know, not wanting to hear.

'I promised I'd take her to the new restaurant that opened up in Wetherton last month.' He paused. 'We leave for Switzerland tomorrow. Go and make things up with your father, Cassie. Decide for yourself what you mean to do. I shan't be around long enough to help.'

He was icily remote now, cold as stone. The breath snagged in her lungs. She had not even dented his rigid self-possession. Desperately, she fought to control the sickening lurch of her stomach. How could he kiss her like that, and then send her away as though the episode had no meaning? For her, the whole world had crystallised in that tender moment of possession. But for him...

She was fooling herself, wasn't she? There was
no place in his life for her. He was making that
plain. He was a man on the move, his parameters
were extending far beyond anything she could
imagine, and he would not be taking her along with
him. Why should he, when the Sophies of this world
beckoned, enticing him with their smooth
sophistication?

If she had any pride left at all she could not let
him see how much he had hurt her by his rejection.

'I'll do that, Ryker,' she said, striving to keep
her voice steady. 'But you already know what I plan
to do, don't you? I'm going away, to study
journalism.'

It was best, she thought achingly, if their paths
crossed only fleetingly from now on. Every time
she saw him, she would have to steel herself not to
care.

Her glance went to the planking and the tool bag.
'I'll leave you to get on,' she said.

He nodded. 'Yes, I'd better make a start. It
wouldn't do to keep Sophie waiting, would it?'

She turned and walked away from him. His knife-
thrust had found its mark, and she knew that the
wound would fester indefinitely, for there was no
cure for a bleeding heart.

In the steamy atmosphere of the bathroom, she
finished dressing in clean blue jeans and a soft
cotton blouse, then pulled a comb through the
damp tendrils of her hair. One thing had not
changed in all these years, she decided morosely.

Sophie was still around. She even had her own key to his apartment.

A door banged somewhere, and she hoped that it meant the other woman had gone at last. Half an hour at a time was about all she could take of her company.

Deftly she applied a light touch of blusher to her cheeks, and searched through her make-up bag for lipstick. Satisfied at last with her reflection in the mirror, she dabbed a splash of her favourite perfume on her wrists and temples before going in search of Ryker. There was still the thorny subject of the air display to be dealt with, and the story her editor wanted, and she knew from past experience it was not a prospect to be relished.

She found him in a small room off the lounge that served as a study. He was sitting at a desk, frowning in concentration as he sifted through some papers.

'Are you busy?' she murmured, seating herself on the arm of his chair and looking over his shoulder at the documents that were occupying his attention. 'That looks technical. Am I in your way?'

He gave her a sideways glance. 'Even if you were, I doubt anything I said would make much difference. Once you're set on something, you can be remarkably persistent.'

She smiled and leaned forward a little, a faint cloud of perfume wafting between them as she rested one arm lightly on the back of the chair. 'Is that a bad thing?' Running her gaze over his strong profile, she resisted the temptation to slide her fingers over the tough sinews of his neck, to explore the texture of crisp dark hair at his nape.

'Not necessarily. It all depends what it is that you're after.'

'Honestly, Ryker,' she murmured, 'to hear you talk, anyone would think I always had an ulterior motive. I'm merely taking an interest in your work.'

'You're up to something. I know you too well.'

'And you're far too suspicious. It can't be good for you. It knots up the muscles, causes tension.' She moved restlessly. Perhaps sitting next to him hadn't been such a good idea. She was the one getting knotted up. He was so close, yet, for all that, he might have been light years away when it came to touching him.

'Lay it on the line, Cassie,' he said abruptly. 'I have work to do, and a meeting scheduled for half an hour's time.'

She grimaced. 'OK—but you have to give it some thought, not just deny me outright.'

His eyes narrowed, and she went on quickly, 'I'd like an interview. Your work, your life, the flying. The air show's next week, isn't it? I could do a full-page spread——'

'No.'

'But you can't dismiss it out of hand, Ryker,' she said urgently. 'It'll be a wonderful article, I promise. I'll even let you go through it before I hand it over. And think how it will enhance your image—how many people know about the pursuits centres you set up, for instance?'

'I started those centres before I went into the charter business,' he said grimly. 'I don't need the extra publicity, especially not the kind of in-depth article you're planning.'

'But you——'

'No.' Ryker's hands gripped her arms, and she registered the familiar aching hurt of rejection as he pushed her away from him. He stood up, moving over to the window, his features all hard angles, shadowed planes.

'I'm warning you, Cassie,' he gritted, 'you are not to write about me. Nor do I want you and that camera-happy sidekick anywhere near me at the air show. Is that clear?'

She got to her feet, swallowing against the painful constriction of her throat. 'Why?' she demanded huskily, endeavouring to batten down her turbulent emotions. 'Give me a reason,' she said. 'You can't still blame me for the articles that have gone out before. I told you, I had nothing to do with what Nick wrote. Besides, he's bound to be there, taking photos of the planes. You can hardly stop him from doing that. The event has to be covered, after all.'

'It's the way he chooses to go about it that concerns me.' He pulled a couple of newspapers from a drawer in his desk and slammed them down in front of her. 'He didn't exactly restrain himself there, did he?'

She looked down at the photograph splashed over one page. Ryker was pictured leaving a cottage with a woman—someone Cassie did not recognise. She read the caption and stifled a groan. 'Haldene leaves cosy love nest. Who is the mystery woman?'

'That was worth a full-page spread, wasn't it?' he bit out.

'I'm sorry,' she said. 'I had no idea. I hadn't seen it. Who is she?' She could not stop herself from asking the question.

'A friend,' he answered tersely. 'Someone I was helping out. What happens next? Headlines in the Sunday papers—"My taste in women, by Ryker Haldene. Secrets from between the sheets."'

She felt her fingers bite into the leather of the chair. 'Ryker, listen to me, will you? You've had your fair share of trouble with the Press, I concede that, and I can understand your attitude. But I'm only trying to do my job. I'd never write anything that would be hurtful to you, you know that.'

'Is that right? And has Jim Harker changed his tactics one iota since he took over at the *Despatch*? We both know he hasn't.' His expression was implacable. 'I've told you,' he said brusquely, 'keep away.'

He was demanding the impossible, she reflected bleakly. She had a job to do, and, one way or another, she had to produce something that would satisfy her boss. Knowing Jim Harker's brittle personality, it was either that, or the dole queue. She had to feed herself and pay the bills, and it was unfortunate that Ryker's strictures came a poor second in that competition.

CHAPTER FOUR

CASSIE watched the plane spiral downwards, her throat taut with anxiety as it swooped towards the ground, the plume of smoke blazoned across the heavens in its wake like a bright streamer. At the very last moment, it seemed, the nose lifted, arcing upwards, on and on into a perfect circle drawn against the backcloth of an intensely blue sky.

Her lungs were painfully constricted. Why did she let it get to her this way? Ryker was a brilliant pilot. Nothing could happen to him, could it? He had nerves of steel, and he knew what he was doing, knew the exact moment to send his craft into a mind-shattering spin.

She swallowed. Now he was banking away, getting ready to bring the plane on course to land.

'I want to get some close-ups,' Nick said at her side. 'We'll have to make our way to the enclosure.'

Cassie nodded, waiting until the gleaming, silver-winged machine coasted along the runway in the distance, and then she let out a long, shuddery breath. 'OK. I'm with you.'

It was just as well there was little more to be done this afternoon. She wouldn't be sorry to be finished here; she was strangely on edge today, had been, in fact, since she had left Ryker's flat. Or perhaps it was just the heat, sapping her of her usual verve. She would be thankful to get away from the crowds, and back to her own place.

Now, though, she had to keep her mind firmly on work. She had already interviewed the various celebrities of the day—all except one, she reflected wryly—and she checked that her notebook was safely tucked into her bag, before she started off after Nick. With luck, Ryker would have unbent enough to give one or two quotes, but she wasn't counting on it, considering his black mood when last she had seen him.

The faintest breeze fanned her hot face as she approached the enclosure with Nick, and she welcomed its cool drift. Showing their Press cards to the officials, they wandered in among the assortment of planes just as Ryker was climbing down from his own. Immediately he was surrounded by a small entourage, and the whole group began to move away towards the refreshments lounge.

He had not noticed Cassie, but of course he wouldn't, she thought with a hint of sourness as she observed Sophie winding her arm through his. The woman couldn't even wait until they were alone together before she started mauling him.

Deliberately, she turned her thoughts to the article she was working on. At least she could go and talk to the mechanic, now that Ryker was otherwise engaged. She left Nick to snap away where his fancy took him, while she went over to talk to the man who had begun a routine check of the plane.

He was more than willing to chat, she discovered, and it seemed that he knew quite a lot about Ryker's private life. She found herself wistfully hoping that he was merely embroidering reality, and at the same time she mentally cursed Jim Harker for putting her through this misery. She would stick to facts about the aircraft and his skill as a pilot. There was no way she could write anything else.

'That was a great one,' Nick said, adjusting the lens on his camera. 'Lean back against the fuselage, both of you, and I'll get another.' She hadn't noticed Nick's reappearance while she had been engrossed in conversation, but now she obliged briefly with a smile, and Nick quickly took the shot he wanted.

Hitching the camera over his shoulder once more, he came and put his arm around her waist. Unexpectedly, giving her no time for evasion, his head swooped downwards and he kissed her. When he finally released her mouth, she stared up at him in faint astonishment. Why had he done that now, in full view of anyone who cared to watch?

She wished that she could feel more for Nick, respond to him in the way that he so obviously wanted. For her, it had been a relief to see a familiar face when they had met up in London. She had just started in her new job, and they had begun to date, and she had tried so hard to make it work between them. But always, deep inside, something made her hold back, some lingering ember, perhaps, of that other fierce chemistry that burned within...

'How about a drink before I get this lot back to the lab?' he murmured, his hands spreading lightly over her ribcage.

'She doesn't have time for that. She and I have some unfinished business to settle.' The harsh words gave her a fierce jolt, and she turned her head, eyes widening, to look up at Ryker, who had appeared at her side out of nowhere like a prowling, malevolent tiger. Her colour must have fluctuated visibly as her temperature shot from hot to cold to hot again in the space of seconds under the needling ferocity of his stare.

With an effort, she began to assemble her scattered wits. 'Unfinished—what business? I don't recall——'

'No, you wouldn't,' he cut in savagely. 'Though if you could manage to stop making an exhibition of yourself for as long as five minutes at a time and prise yourself away from Casonova here, you might find you have less trouble with your memory.' He looked at Nick as though he might hit him, then turned on the white-faced mechanic.

'Don't you have work to be getting on with?' he gritted.

The young man made an expedient, hasty exit, and Cassie frowned after his disappearing figure. 'Was it necessary to use that tone with him?' she demanded.

'It wouldn't have been if you hadn't gone out of your way to distract him.' His attention swung blackly to Nick's hand, still draped around her waist. 'Are you having trouble ungluing yourself from Cassandra or were you waiting for me to do it for you?' His eyes burned with glittering menace, and slowly Cassie felt Nick's fingers slip away.

'You have no right,' she flung at Ryker, clenching her teeth. It wasn't as though he cared about her, was it? He just wanted to get at Nick. 'Who gave you the idea you could interfere? What business is it of yours?'

'Feeling deprived, are you?' he said, with a sneer, and her fingers itched to slap him. He had a nerve pouring condemnation on her when he had only just torn himself away from Sophie's clutches. The thought of them together made her stomach turn. 'I wouldn't advise it,' he said darkly, staring at her hands. 'I just may hit back.'

'Now look here...' Nick began, only to find himself pinned like a squirming insect under the sharp lance of Ryker's gaze.

'Still here, Driscoll?' he mouthed unpleasantly.

Nick backed off a little, and Cassie said tautly, 'You're the one who should be leaving, Ryker. Your presence is not required. You've already set a spanner in the works—isn't that enough to satisfy even you?'

'Not nearly enough,' he growled. 'You have some explaining to do.'

She ignored the dark storm raging in his eyes and glared back. 'Oh, you think so, do you? Why is that? Are you suffering some kind of ego trip?'

'Cassie,' Nick said, placing a restraining hand on her arm, 'perhaps you should——'

'Keep out of this, Nick,' she seethed, slapping his hand away, and turning with renewed belligerence towards Ryker. 'Since when do I have to account to you for my actions?'

'Since your seedy, underhand enquiries were aimed at winkling out whatever information you could get from my mechanic.'

'Seedy? Underhand?' Her tone dripped scorn. 'Look around, why don't you? This is broad daylight, or hadn't you noticed? Perhaps it's your mind that's the problem. Too many dark corners in there, with lurking monsters creeping and crawling around.'

He didn't like that. Long, hard fingers came around her wrist like a manacle, clamping the slender bones, and pulling her away from the relative protection of the plane. She had forgotten just how strong he was.

'We'll finish this conversation somewhere else,' he said, his face set like granite. 'Come on.'

Nick moved, and Ryker's teeth bared in a snarl. 'Any interference from you, Driscoll, and you'll find yourself very swiftly in no man's land.'

Nick hesitated, and Cassie could see that there would be no help forthcoming from that quarter. It served her right for slapping him away. Her breath hissed in frustration. She was on her own.

Digging her heels into the tarmac, she jerked her wrist ineffectually against the hand that held her. She was no match for him, and her temper soared as he dragged her along after him.

'I'm not going anywhere with you, you oversized bully. Who do you think you are, Haldene, coming here and throwing your weight about?' Enraged, she clenched her free hand into a fist against her side until the knuckles whitened with the strain. 'Don't think you can come here telling me what do do. If I want to wander about chatting to all and sundry I'll do it, with our without your say-so.'

Her words made no impact on him, and she was uncomfortably aware that people were beginning to turn their heads and stare after them as he propelled her across the tarmac to the car park. 'People are looking, Ryker,' she gritted fiercely. 'You're making a scene. Doesn't that bother you?'

'I'm getting used to it, around you,' he slammed back. 'You and trouble seem to be synonymous.'

Reaching his car, he opened the passenger door, and pushed her inside so that she sprawled in an untidy heap on the leather. Before she had even managed to straighten out her limbs, he had the engine up and running.

'Damn you, Ryker, you'll pay for this. This is the second time you've abducted me. It's getting to be a fetish.'

'Sure,' he said nastily. 'I can think of a few others I could get hooked on. All I need to start is a gag and a length of strong rope.'

Her teeth clamped. 'I didn't know you had such sadistic tendencies. Turns you on, does it, getting rough with helpless women?'

She felt his cynical gaze rake over her flushed features. 'You? Helpless? Don't make me laugh,'

he mouthed tersely. 'You'd scare off a snake if it
threatened your space.'

'Oh, that's great,' she said, stung by his harsh
opinion of her. 'So now I'm some kind of Amazon,
am I?'

'You're a rebel,' he said rigorously. 'You always
have been. Ever since I've known you, you've lit
up like a fuse in a box of fireworks whenever
anyone challenged your right to do as you pleased.
Don't you ever think of the consequences for other
people?'

Her brows arched finely. 'I have no idea how you
came by this bad opinion of me. Since when did I
do anything to hurt anyone else?'

'Going behind my back and getting information
out of my mechanic wasn't exactly designed to
overwhelm me with joy, was it?'

They had reached their destination, it seemed.
Ryker swung the car violently into the only parking
space available in the vicinity of a country pub and
they climbed out on to the gravelled drive.

'Is it my fault he was such a blabber-mouth?' she
said. 'All I did was chat about the plane. I didn't
ask him to volunteer details about your sleazy love-
life.' In fact she desperately wished he hadn't.
Details were the last thing she wanted to know.
'Though how you have the nerve to throw stones
at me and Nick with your sheets glowing from all
the heat generated I don't know. If you don't want
your linen aired in public, you should try being
more discreet.'

'My love-life is not sleazy. You shouldn't believe everything you're told.'

He marched her across the gravel and the smell of burgers being grilled on a barbecue made her feel faintly nauseous. With Ryker continually rocking the see-saw of her emotions, how could she ever face food again?

Her glance took in the busy forecourt. The place overlooked open fields and the drone of aircraft could be heard overhead as the air display continued. It was a hive of industry out here. People were collecting beer and snacks and heading along the footpath to the field to watch the show in comfort.

'Full, then,' she said thinly. 'Would that be a better word? Let's say your flat sees a lot of activity, with Sophie flitting in and out at all hours.' Pain stabbed at her and she went on with remorseless sarcasm, 'Not to mention all the others.'

His eyes slitted. 'You're treading on thin ice, lady. I've told you before, you shouldn't put any credence in what you read. Especially what's printed in your own paper.'

'Oh, of course,' she said, nodding in arrant disbelief. 'Well, you would say that, wouldn't you? What have you done with Sophie, by the way? I see you eventually managed to tear yourself away from her arms.'

He frowned. 'Sophie is not your concern. She merely dropped by on her way to meet some friends. She never intended to stay.'

'Hah!' Cassie exploded in sickly triumph. 'So you're the one who's feeling deprived. Now I know what this is all about. You're working out your frustration by lashing out at me. Too bad, Ryker. You'll just have to suffer.' Though she doubted his suffering would ever reach the depths she had plumbed.

'Don't be ridiculous.' He dug in his pocket for some change and ordered a couple of drinks from the outdoor sales. 'That's all beside the point, anyway. The fact is, I won't have you printing a load of rubbish about me.'

'As if I would.' His accusation made her blood boil. She felt the angry hurt fizzing inside her. 'Didn't I tell you I'd show you the copy first? What do you take me for, Ryker?'

'I think,' he said bitingly, 'that you're going out of your way to annoy me, buzzing away like a gnat that won't give up till it gets its bite of flesh. All that matters to you is getting a story at all costs. You were defeated over the squat, and you're determined not to lose out this time. Well, I'm here to tell you, you're not going to wheedle any more information out of anyone even remotely connected with me. My private life is my own; you're not going to spread it over the papers for all and sundry to pick at.'

'Thanks a lot,' she said bitterly, incensed and profoundly wounded by his casual summing-up of her character. 'As a matter of fact I did manage to produce an article on the squat, despite your interference, and it was very well received. And as to any writing about your private life, it wouldn't occur to you that your reasoning is at all faulty, would it? I've never set out to write anything bad about you. I'm sorry if Jim slants things the wrong way, but I don't go out of my way to cause you trouble, and it won't happen again, believe me.'

'I don't believe you.'

Her fingers clenched. 'It seems to me that you're determined to think the worst of me, no matter what I say or do.'

'*Especially* what you do,' he agreed savagely, tossing aside her attempt at explanation in a casual way that made her madder still. How could he have the nerve to decry her actions when he had just hijacked her?

Taking a long swallow from his beer, he thrust a drink into her hand, and for a wild moment she contemplated tipping it over him.

'Don't even think it,' he advised with taut menace, his own glass raised and ready.

Her lips flattened against her teeth. She didn't doubt that he'd do it.

He finished his drink and pushed the empty glass on to a table by the barbecue before turning towards the footpath. Did he expect her to follow? Stubbornly, she held her ground. She was astounded by the way his thinking processes were working. How could he believe her capable of such malice?

'Are you going to stay there all day?' he demanded.

'I'm considering my options,' she said. Thirstily, she drank the last of the cold cider and slammed down her glass. 'You can't seriously think I'm going to meekly trail after you so that you can continue the lecture. Just because you dragged me to this place doesn't have to mean I'm stranded.'

Broodingly, she glanced over to the car. Had he locked it? Was there the slightest chance he still kept a spare key hidden in the glove compartment? It would serve him right if his car disappeared from under his nose. Three or four minutes were all she needed.

Her dark thoughts were interrupted by the unmistakable jangle of his keys. Tormentingly, he held them out on one finger. His mouth twisted in sardonic amusement. 'You'll have to wrestle me for them.'

'You think you're so clever, don't you?' she said tightly. 'Watch your step, Ryker. You're heading for a fall.'

'Then I'll take you down with me,' he said, his voice grim.

A jet screamed overhead and they both looked up to follow its progress, shielding their eyes from the sun.

Ryker shifted abruptly. 'It's pointless standing here arguing,' he said. 'We might as well go down to the field to watch the last part of the show.'

She didn't move, and his eyes took on a steely glint. 'If you tamper with the car, you'll set off the alarm. Don't say I didn't warn you.'

He started along the footpath and after a few moody seconds of debate she went after him, picking her way over the rough ground towards the stile. Everything was going wrong, and it was all her own fault. She had made him angry by turning up this afternoon, but what else could she do? Her job was at stake. Hooking her jeans-clad leg over the wooden bar, she wondered if there was any way she could persuade him to see things from her point of view.

She manoeuvred over the stile, and when her feet touched the solid earth once more she paused for a moment, staring about her at the lush stretch of meadow. It was festooned with groups of people— couples, families with young children—all intent on making the most of the summer afternoon. There were picnic baskets scattered around, she noticed, and bottles of squash, and some people had binoculars to help them keep track of the planes droning at intervals overhead.

'I should be covering the rest of the show,' she said, going over to where Ryker had settled himself.

'Knowing you, you've already three times as much as you need.' He plucked a long blade of grass, twirling it idly in his fingers.

Dropping to sit beside him, she said, 'I really haven't any intention of writing anything that could possibly offend you.' Her mouth made a grimace. 'That's a promise, Ryker. I thought I'd concentrate the bulk of my article on the charity aspect.'

He sent her a cool glance, his jaw tightening. 'Your word had better be good.' He stretched out his long legs, and leaned back on his elbow, studying the swirling path of a biplane as it looped in the sky. 'When is the piece supposed to be featured?' he asked brusquely.

She glanced at him quickly. 'Tomorrow. I'll type it up later this afternoon and take it into the office as soon as it's ready. Most likely it will go out in the weekend edition as well. It won't take Nick long to process the photos.'

Distaste etched his features. 'He hangs around you like a pet poodle. Seems to me he's been clinging to your skirts since you were knee-high to a grasshopper.'

'I was away for three years,' she retorted. 'A lot of water's gone under the bridge in that time.' He was never going to let her forget that momentary indiscretion with Nick, was he?

'He's still around. He must have homed in on you as soon as he discovered you were in London.'

Her gaze was withering. 'We were bound to meet—we were mixing in the same circles. And now we work together, hadn't you noticed?'

'Is that what you call it? It didn't look much like work to me, the way he was wrapping himself around you.'

His tone was sneering, and she stiffened, but he hadn't finished. 'Has he moved in with you yet, or is that a delight still to come?'

'You never give up, do you?' she said tersely. 'It may be the casual sort of arrangement you'd go in for, but I want more than that.'

'Ah. You want him to do the honourable thing.' His eyes narrowed, the pupils darkening. 'Is that likely?'

'He's already proposed,' she said tautly. 'Does that satisfy your curiosity?'

Ryker's jaw clenched. 'You can't marry him. It would be the biggest mistake you ever made.'

'Why? Because you don't approve of him? The decision is mine to make.' The fact that she had turned him down need not come into it. She had known Nick for some time, but her emotions remained locked up inside her. He had tried to persuade her that love would grow if she gave it half a chance, and she had tried, but it made no difference in the end. But Ryker had no right to intrude. Who was he to judge her when it came to relationships?

'Because of your background. Some day, you're going to be a very rich young woman. When does the full bequest from your grandparents come to you? When you reach the age of twenty-five, or when you marry; isn't that the situation? And isn't there some kind of shares set-up?'

'And if there is?'

'Don't you see it makes all the difference?'

'No, I don't.' She frowned. 'Nick said he wanted to marry me. The money isn't an issue between us.'

'If you think that, then you're a fool,' he said sharply.

Cassie hesitated. Ryker had his own reasons for questioning Nick's integrity, and it would be fatal to her peace of mind if she let him believe he had planted a seed of doubt. His ego was big enough already.

'I don't want to discuss the subject,' she said.

The tension was back between them in full force, the air bristling with it, and she could not understand her own confused and troubled feelings. She glanced at Ryker's taut profile. Did he find her so unattractive that he could not understand that a man could care for her deeply? Certainly she held no appeal for him; he had made that clear years ago, and at his flat the other day—hadn't he pushed her away from him? He had even, this afternoon, she thought ruefully, compared her to a gnat.

Another plane circled the skies above them, and Ryker tilted his head back, focusing his attention on the display with the curiosity of one expert in the skill of another.

She stared at him through heavy-lidded eyes, absorbed by the way the white denim of his trousers moulded itself to his strong thighs, the way the navy T-shirt clung faithfully to his muscled chest and the flat plane of his stomach. Her glance stole to his face, and she had to curb her desperate impulse to reach out and trace the line of his jaw. Why was he so remote from her? Why did they always have to argue?

The faintly spicy fragrance of his aftershave mingled with his own indefinable clean male scent. He was near enough to her so that she could see the texture of his skin, the firmly rounded outline of his mouth, yet, for all that, there was a wall between them that could never be breached.

Her gaze jerked away like a skittish foal, small beads of perspiration breaking out on her brow. What was wrong with her? Her thoughts had gone shooting off on a crazy, outlandish track and it was all she could do to get herself under control. She was behaving like an idiot, running after something way beyond her reach. Pensively, she smoothed her fingers over the denim of her jeans. Would he ever allow her to get close to him?

Restlessly she eased her position on the grass, curling her legs beneath her. Crying for the moon was a wearing occupation; there had to be something she could do to take away the dull ache inside. It was time she took her life in hand again.

The whine of the aircraft diminished to a low throb as the plane became a mere speck in the distance, and Ryker turned to look at her. 'I feel like stretching my legs,' he said. 'Are you coming?'

He stood up, his body long and lithe, and put out a hand to pull her to her feet. To him, it was just a polite gesture, but its effect on Cassie was immediate. She could feel the ricochet of pleasure vibrating along her spine.

'How long are you staying in the area?' she asked as they set off across the field to find the footpath.

'Another day or so. I have some things to attend to and then I'm going to spend a short time at one of the pursuits centres.'

'I'd heard that.' Drat Jim Harker and his wretched story.

They had reached a wooden fence, and again he held out a hand to her as she climbed over. The touch of his fingers was like flame on her skin, the imprint burning in her mind long after he had released her. A stream flowed through the field, and they walked alongside it, Ryker's gaze fixed on the burbling, tumbling water.

She cast him a considering glance. 'I wonder,' she began slowly, 'if you would let me come along?'

He viewed her with suspicion. 'Why the sudden interest?'

'Hardly sudden,' she protested. 'It's been at the back of my mind for some time.' She grinned faintly. 'I've always thought it would be interesting to see you in action, but you weren't around to ask. Anyway,' she went on more soberly, 'Jim heard you were going and he asked me to write a piece on you and the centres, and how you came to set them up.'

'I knew it,' he drawled. 'I knew your sudden interest had some connection with your work.'

'It isn't purely because of my work,' she said.

His gaze was sceptical. 'It seems to me that the only reason for your persistence is your ruthless determination to please your editor.'

'I do have to earn a living,' she said, annoyed that he had put her on the defensive. 'But all the same, the idea does appeal to me. I think I'd quite like to immerse myself in an environment that's wild and natural and totally alien to me, something right away from the city, and the traffic, and the pollution.'

'Book yourself a holiday in the outback. That should do the trick.'

'Now you're being facetious,' she said irritably, pained by his dismissal of her. Was the thought of having her near him for any length of time so distasteful to him? 'Why are you so against me all the time? There's no reason why I shouldn't go along. It might do me a world of good—aren't these courses designed to instil self-confidence?'

'You don't need any boost to your confidence. You have more than enough already.'

She pulled a face. 'Not true,' she said. 'There's always room for improvement. What could be better for me than to join the group you'll be taking?'

'You wouldn't fit in with them.'

'Why not?' she demanded.

'They're all young men.'

'You're a chauvinist. Don't you know about equality? Women no longer spend all their time sewing samplers and singing by the piano; you do realise that, don't you? Some of us even hold down steady jobs, run a home, and, heaven forbid, drive a car.'

'Some of you,' he countered drily, 'even manage to keep the car maintained regularly so it doesn't let you down every five minutes.'

She coloured faintly. 'It isn't my fault if you men keep changing the rules. If you will insist on bringing in lead-free petrol you should see to it that all the engines work on it. Or at least keep the pumps in a separate place where people in a hurry don't get confused.'

Ryker gave a smothered cough and she sent him a sharp stare. 'Don't you dare laugh at me.'

His mouth twitched. 'I wouldn't dream of it.'

Stopping beneath the shade of a huge old sycamore, he stared down into the stream, watching the frenetic passage of the water as it cascaded in darting whorls over the weathered stones.

'Why do you keep saying no to me, Ryker?' Cassie asked huskily, coming to stand beside him, her spine angled lightly against the bark of the tree, her eyes unconsciously wide with appeal. 'It's just a little article. Just an interesting feature on what it feels like to take part on one of these courses. I give you my word, I'd be no trouble. You wouldn't even know I was there.'

'Your word, huh?' He flattened his hand against the tree and studied her thoughtfully. 'I think you could turn out to be more trouble than I ever envisaged.' He reached for her hand. 'You're no longer a tomboy, Cassie. You're a city girl, through and through. You've been pampered all your life.'

Slowly, he turned her fingers for his inspection. His thumb brushed softly, feather-light, over her palm, and a trembling started up inside her. She tried to stem the quivering reaction of her body. He didn't know what his touch was doing to her. How could he? Yet her limbs were molten; she was weak with sudden longing.

'Look at these hands,' he murmured. 'They're beautiful, manicured to perfection. How long do you think they'd stay that way?' He shook his head.

'At the first sign of discomfort, you'll be agitating to come home.'

Her eyes darkened. 'You don't know that. You might at least give me the chance to prove myself.'

He released her hand. 'You don't have to prove anything, Cassie.'

'Please, Ryker? Don't refuse me. I want to do a serious piece.'

'Even if you did, there's no guarantee Harker wouldn't turn it around.' He shook his head. 'Besides, as I said, the group is all male. Perhaps you could go along some other time, with no input for the paper.' He watched her expression. 'I'm sorry.'

'No, you're not,' she said fiercely. 'You're glad to have the chance to turn me down. You don't want me around because you think I'll cause problems. I won't, I promise. Anyway, you've taken women along before, I know you have.'

'Women,' he agreed, amicably enough. 'Not one woman, not you. You'd create too much of a diversion. I don't want you around, causing havoc.'

Her cheeks dimpled. 'Me—havoc? Now how could I do that? You know I wouldn't dream of upsetting the apple cart.'

His smile was fixed. 'Coming from the lips of Eve's handmaiden, that does nothing to reassure me. You've been practising since childhood.'

She laughed softly, but it was a wistful laugh, directed at herself. If he thought her capable of disturbing other men, why was it that she couldn't have that effect on him?

'You think so?'

He leaned towards her, a faint, answering smile on that dangerously attractive mouth, and her senses reeled, heady with a peculiar, aching excitement. Hazily, she wished that she could feel the sensuous drift of those firm lips on hers. Her breath spun out in a long, soundless sigh. The sun danced lightly over her skin; she felt the heat of it seeping into her limbs and filling her with a deep, melting languor.

Carefully she rested her head back against the tree, her soft curls spreading out in a cloudy fan about her head.

His glance narrowed on her. 'There are tiny leaves in your hair,' he said. 'You must have brushed by the hedgerow when you climbed the stile.'

The warm amber gleam of his eyes explored her features, traced the pattern of her mouth, her cheekbones, rested on the soft down of her skin. He was so close that he might almost have touched her. She found herself aching for the feel of his fingers firm about her ribcage, the brush of his hand over the waiting silk of her flesh. Fierce longing rippled through her veins. Her body arched faintly in reckless acknowledgement of her need, and his gaze wandered over the heated flush of her skin, came to dwell on the full pink curve of her mouth.

His features shaded, the planes and angles of his face dark and shuttered.

'Go back, Cassie,' he said, and there was a harsh, mocking inflexion in his voice as he moved away from her. She was bereft, stunned. 'Tell Jim Harker that there's no deal. No trip. No story.'

He started to walk along the path that led back to the car, and Cassie closed her eyes, absorbing the impact of the shock on her bewildered senses, trying desperately to focus on reality. How could she have left herself open once more to his callous indifference to her? When would she ever learn the lesson he had been trying to teach her throughout all those long, empty years? He did not want her. He would never want her.

As she sank back against the tree, the rough bark on her spine and beneath her fingers was like a scourge, underlining her folly. She should never have let her emotions get the better of her. The flame of love was fickle; it turned in on her and scorched her soul, leaving only ashes in its place. If she was to survive, she had to stifle the blaze before it raged out of control and consumed her altogether. But how was she to do that?

Work was her only salvation. Unfortunate that it must also involve Ryker, but what choice did she have? Jim was determined on this new angle, and that meant, vetoed or not, Ryker's island pursuits centre had to be her next port of call.

CHAPTER FIVE

ONCE made, there was no going back on her decision to join Ryker on the island. Cassie tried to push back the feelings of guilt that assailed her. Jim Harker had refused to listen to sweet reason, and she had thought long and hard about telling him what to do with his job, before concluding dismally that other offers of employment would be few and far between in the present climate.

It was just like Jim to have winkled out all the details of Ryker's travel plans, and Cassie already knew where he moored his sleek launch. Slipping on board in the first light of morning, without attracting attention, had been more than a little wearing on her nerves, she recalled. Even now, her heart was still pounding at the prospect of discovery.

Luckily the large mound of canvas sheeting on deck provided a reasonable refuge, though if she had to stay cooped up like this much longer she'd be too stiff to move, and that wouldn't do at all. She needed to be pretty swift on her feet if she was to keep out of Ryker's way for the next few hours. He would find out soon enough that she'd stowed away on board, but, if things went to plan, by the time all hell was let loose it would be too late for him to ship her back home.

Risking a glance from under the heavy weatherproof sheet, she was thankful to see the island come into view. She was hungry—it must be nearing breakfast-time—but she would have to wait a while before she could eat. Avoiding Ryker was top priority for the moment. Though, as he didn't own the island, he hardly had the right to forbid her presence there, and if she happened to be always in the outer edges of his vision as he worked with his group of men there was probably little he could do about it.

He was guiding the boat carefully alongside its mooring by a rough wooden quay. A few more minutes, and she would be able to free her cramped legs and get the circulation going once more.

She waited while he unloaded supplies, and as soon as he had heaved the last box from the deck and marched away with it she hauled herself stiffly on to dry land. Even at this early hour, the heat was beginning to build up, and she looked at the sky and hoped there wouldn't be a storm later on. Pulling her overloaded holdall across her shoulders, she pondered which direction to take. Ryker had headed east. It followed, therefore, that she should turn to the west.

It was a relatively small island. She could do a swift reconnaissance of his camp later, when he had settled everyone in. Though where the others actually were was something of a mystery. Perhaps they would be arriving later—an unusual divergence from the normal procedure, she would have thought, but no doubt there was a perfectly reasonable explanation.

An hour later, she stood on the cliff edge, looking bleakly out over the sea crashing against the rocks below. The island had a stark beauty, with grassy hillocks, and rocky outcrops, and a freshwater brook running through a winding vale. Behind her, a small copse offered a modicum of shelter. Perhaps she would rig up something there for the night. Shrugging to ease the tension in her shoulders and back, she turned her thoughts firmly to the preparations she needed to make.

'What the devil are you doing here?'

Cassie froze, rooted to the spot by the savagely familiar tones. How had he managed to discover her so soon? she groaned inwardly. Couldn't she have had just another hour, at least?

'Answer me, damn you.'

Slowly, she turned around, steeling herself. 'Why, if it isn't Ryker,' she murmured. 'What a small world it is.'

'Don't try to be flippant with me.' The biting fury of his tone sliced through her like a knife, and she had to brace herself not to flinch. 'How the hell did you get here?'

She sent him a cool stare. 'The same way as you,' she answered. 'It seemed the logical way to travel at the time.'

'Did it indeed?' He started towards her, menacing her with his taut, muscled frame. 'Let me tell you,' he said through his teeth, 'your logic has a major flaw—namely, I don't like it. I don't need it. I won't have it messing up my plans. Am I making myself clear?'

'Perfectly.' He was still advancing on her slowly, with lethal precision, like a tiger stalking his prey. She eyed his long, powerful body with misgiving, and took a careful step backwards.

'I have no intention of "messing up your plans" as you put it. I'm here to do a little quiet research. Just pretend I'm not here, that I don't exist.'

'My life's ambition,' he grated. 'Only it's becoming all too apparent that you're out to do whatever you can to sabotage my dreams.' A muscle flicked in his jaw. 'What is it with you? Are you determined to go to any lengths to get a story?' His mouth made a sardonic curve. 'Well, your luck just ran out. This is the end of the line. You'd better grab your things and come with me.'

Defiantly, she stood her ground. 'I don't need you to tell me what to do,' she threw back tightly.

'Don't you?' He moved, swifter than light, his hand clamping her wrist. 'I have to disagree.'

'Let go of me,' she flared, struggling furiously, losing her balance as the soft earth shifted beneath her feet. 'Take your macho tactics some place else.'

He glanced over the cliff top, at the tumbling waves below, his lips making a brief, cold smile. 'Do you really want me to let you go?'

She followed his glance, a small shiver of unease rippling along her spine. She did not like the undercurrent of malice in his tone. He looked, she thought, as though he might actually enjoy dropping her over the edge.

'Take a closer look down there,' he gritted. 'Why do you think those stones are heaped up at the foot of the cliff? Like to join them, would you? Believe me, right now that would cause me very little heartache.'

Suddenly, the ground no longer felt quite so stable. Horrified, she realised that something was happening, that what she had thought was rock-solid was in fact beginning to break up beneath her feet. She felt the earth give way, felt herself begin to slip down, the toes of her shoes scrabbling against rock to find a narrow ledge. The blood drained away from her face. It was only the iron band of his fingers that held her secure, prevented her from falling.

'Ryker,' she said hoarsely, struggling frantically to keep her balance on the crumbling earth, 'I think—er—I think this is—er—some kind of land-slip... It isn't safe——'

'You said it.' His fingers gripped her like a vice. 'Not quite so self-assured now, are you, Cassandra? Do you still want me to let you go?'

'N-no. Ryker,' she said in panic, 'don't play games; this is—not funny.'

'You'd rather I helped you?'

She nodded, her eyes widening in desperation. Why was he asking such damn-fool questions?

His teeth bared. 'Say "please, Ryker,"' he drawled with silky intonation. '"Please help me, Ryker." Let me hear you say it.'

She muttered a short, heartfelt prayer as more stones dislodged beneath her feet. 'Please, Ryker,' she whispered. 'Please help me.'

At last he did as she asked. Swinging her into his arms, he lifted her up and away, walking with her to a safe distance from the edge. She clung to him, frantic with remembered terror, her breath coming in short, sharp bursts as her lungs did battle with her rattled nerves.

He set her down on her feet, but still her fingers clutched at him. Her heart was racing, pounding as fiercely as the waves that broke on the jagged rocks below. A shudder racked her body, her hands moving convulsively against his chest.

He pulled her to him, his arms fastening about her, his eyes dark and unreadable before he bent towards her and brushed her trembling mouth with his own.

Tension had locked her limbs, panicked fear still held her mind in thrall, yet gradually the sweet, slow burn of his kiss mingled with the confusion of her thoughts, until after a while the shock of what had happened to her began to ebb away.

Easing her closer to him, he deepened the kiss, pressuring her to him with the taut strength of his thighs, the binding inducement of his hand splayed out in firm possession along her spine.

Conscious thought had flown; there was only this new and bewildering sensation, this seductive, wildfire assault that scorched away the last vestiges of her fright. A tremor rippled through her, a soft sound breaking in her throat.

She felt his hands tighten on her momentarily before he dragged his mouth from hers. Heat flickered in the depths of his gaze, slowly dying away to be replaced by a darkness she could not fathom. He pushed her from him.

Dazed, she stared at him, her lips swollen and tingling from the sweet ravishment he had inflicted. Why had he done that? Why had he kissed her, then pushed her away as though he could not bear her near him? Had it been just a spur-of-the-moment thing, brought on by their sudden closeness? She was a woman, and she had clung to him, and there was no denying he was a strongly physical man; his reactions were swift and overwhelming. What had happened? Had he remembered the only woman who held any place in his life? Had he recalled that his loyalty and affection lay with Sophie?

She swallowed on the acrid taste that welled in her throat. How could he have kissed her like that, after the way he had treated her? He had taken pleasure in taunting her over that sheer drop, in tormenting her. It added insult to injury to be cast aside so readily now.

'How could you treat me like that?' she demanded, bitterness underscoring her voice.

His brow rose, and her anger grew. 'You enjoyed making me suffer,' she accused. 'I was scared out of my wits when I started to slip down that cliffside, and as far as you were concerned I might have been a sack of grain. You didn't care two pins for what I was going through.'

'Perhaps the knowledge that you had brought it on yourself had something to do with that.' His cool response brought her no satisfaction.

'I hate you for what you did,' she threw at him furiously. 'I might have been killed, and you treated it like some kind of a joke.'

'Hardly a joke,' he remarked tautly. 'I find nothing remotely funny in your presence here. I told you not to come, and you deliberately went against what I said.' His brows drew together in a dark, forbidding line. 'These places can be dangerous,' he rasped. 'As you just discovered for yourself. Lucky for you that I happened to be around. They're no playground for a tenderfoot with no training whatsoever.'

'I'm not a total idiot,' she muttered, forced to acknowledge that he had at least saved her from falling. He didn't have to relish her plight so much, though, did he? 'I wouldn't have come here without doing some reading on the subject first——'

'Reading,' he echoed, his tone sharp with derision. 'A lot of good that will do you.'

Smarting, she said, 'You talked to me about some of the survival training you did when you were in the Army...'

A gleam darted fitfully in his eyes. 'That was a long time ago. What were you? An itsy bitsy teenager with——'

'With fluff between her ears—go on, say it,' she said, resenting the easy way he thrust aside her defensive claims. 'That's what you think, isn't it?' She faced him stormily, hands on her hips, ready to do battle. Obviously the long talks they had had all those years ago meant nothing to him, though she remembered them vividly. 'You don't give me any credence,' she railed. 'Well, you'll see. I'll show you.'

Grimly he studied the slim gold watch on his wrist. 'I don't have time to take you back to the mainland now.'

'Forget it,' she said, her mouth taking on a mutinous line. 'I wouldn't go, anyway. I'm here now, and I'm staying. My being here doesn't involve any decision-making on your part.'

'Doesn't it?' His tone was caustic. 'I don't have time to play nursemaid.'

'I can take care of myself.' A faint breeze fanned her hot cheeks, disturbed the thin fabric of her soft cotton shirt. She felt its warm touch on her legs, left bare by her denim shorts.

'Sure. You just gave me a prime example of how you do that. I guess on that record all I have to do is come back in the morning and search for your body.'

His jeering tone scalded her pride. 'Don't bother,' she said. 'Just keep away from me.' Her sparking gaze took in his black jeans and the black T-shirt, the gleaming midnight hair. Why did he have to look so...powerfully male? 'If you hadn't come along threatening me like some kind of dark, avenging demon I wouldn't have strayed so close to the edge in the first place. Leave me alone, Ryker; get off my case.'

'Nothing will give me greater pleasure,' he agreed tersely. 'Return the favour, will you? I have a lot to do, and I don't need you in my hair.'

'I have no intention of getting in your way,' she muttered. 'I'm sure you have more than enough to do seeing to your protégés. No doubt they'll more than appreciate your undivided attention.'

'Which protégés did you have in mind? There's no one here but you and me.'

She stiffened. 'But—you said you were bringing a group.'

'Not to this island, and not for a few days yet. In fact, for your information, you wayward little witch, this is a new location. I'm here to complete a survey, check out the possibilities and pitfalls. As you already discovered, there's a dangerous land-slip that has to be fenced off before we can let loose any raw recruits.' His smile grated on her nerves. 'So it seems,' he murmured, 'that if you were hoping to snatch any more interviews your plans are doomed to disappointment.'

She bit back her chagrin. Getting the thoughts and feelings of all the members of the group might have given her a slant that would take the pressure off Ryker. She could have come up with something to satisfy Jim Harker and at the same time keep Ryker from blowing his top. The whole thing had not sat easy with her right from the beginning, and now it seemed that it had all been for nothing.

'It looks as though Jim had his dates all mixed up,' she said dolefully.

'Doesn't it?' Ryker's obvious satisfaction needled her.

She shrugged. 'Then I shall simply have to concentrate on getting the feel of the place instead. I'll discover what it feels like to combat the elements, and try fending for myself in primitive surroundings.'

'I imagine you'll gain a good idea of that through the course of the day,' he agreed. 'Hunting out something to eat and drink will occupy a lot of your time. Unless, of course, you've stuffed that holdall with goodies.'

His disparaging glance showed he expected that was exactly what she would have done.

'I didn't have room,' she said. 'Other things seemed more important.'

His mouth twisted at that, and she felt a spark of satisfaction.

'I'm sure there's a plentiful harvest out there just awaiting my delectation,' she told him with a confidence she was far from feeling.

'True,' he agreed. 'There are plenty of berries and mushrooms on the island. Nettles, too. Try boiling them.'

'Nettles?' She stared at him. 'Don't you think I could poison myself eating those?'

His eyes glinted. 'Keep away from me if you do. I'd hate to have you throw up all over me.'

She watched as he walked away without a backward glance. That just about summed it up, didn't it? That was as much as he cared. She could drop down the cliff or writhe in agony from tasting some deadly substance, and she was crazy if she expected anything else. He was never going to toss her a declaration of undying love, was he?

This was no time to start feeling sorry for herself. Pulling her notebook and pencil from her bag, she made a few swift jottings. One way or another, she would get an article out of this.

Throughout the morning, she heard Ryker banging away at fence posts, and came across him from time to time as he strung wire in a taut line across the dangerous spots on various parts of the island.

The heat was getting more oppressive as the day wore on. She explored the whole of the west side of the island, taking notes, and collecting dry wood for a fire, so that she could boil up water for a drink. Nettle soup. Ugh. Still, she could give it a try. And Ryker was certainly right about the presence of nettles on the island. Her reddened, stinging legs were testimony to that.

She sat down on a flat rock near to the place where he had moored the boat, and looked up at the darkening sky. Rubbing a hand gingerly over the tender skin, she wondered if there was thunder in the air. Her throat was dry, her skin flushed from her exertions.

'Having second thoughts about your venture into the wilderness?'

She tensed as he came into view. 'Certainly not,' she said sharply. 'It'll take a lot more than your grouchy presence to put me off. If your recruits can put up with you, so can I.'

'Some of them actually enjoy my company.'

She shot him a dark look. 'You mean the women, I suppose. I've no doubt you put yourself out to be charming to them. After all, they do pay for the experience.'

'Careful, Cassie,' he cautioned her. 'Your sharp tongue is getting the better of you.'

She gave him a serenely innocent smile, hiding the nagging jealousy of her thoughts, then turned her gaze in the direction of the shore. Absently, she scratched at the irritation on her legs.

'What have you done?' he asked.

'Nothing.'

He bent down beside her and she swung her legs away from his hard scrutiny. 'Keep still,' he ordered, lightly slapping her thigh, 'and let me look.'

His fingers feathered over her burning calves, and she wasn't altogether sure that the heat she was experiencing came solely from the nettle sting. A faint throbbing started up in her temples; a light ripple of sensation quivered through her limbs.

'It's not as bad as it looks,' he said at last. 'I'll get something to put on it.'

He walked over to the launch, and came back a few minutes later holding a tube of ointment. Unscrewing the lid, he squeezed out a few centimetres of white cream and smoothed it over her skin. The cooling effect gave almost instant relief.

'That feels good,' she said on a sigh. 'Thanks.'

He put the lid back on the tube and dropped it into her holdall. 'If you wore something sensible, instead of flaunting yourself in those cut-off denims, you wouldn't have been stung.'

The rebuke smarted more than the inflamed skin. 'Oh, I'm sorry,' she said tartly, remembering Sophie's painful gibes. 'Is my dress sense not to your taste? I do apologise for offending you. I'll wear a yashmak and robe next time I come on one of these trips.'

'Heaven forbid there's a next time.'

She stood up, sending him a glare. 'I suppose if my name happened to be Sophie you'd have no objections. She could "flaunt herself", as you put it, in whatever she fancied.'

'I doubt very much that Sophie would want to be here, roughing it,' he said drily, 'let alone allow herself to be seen dead in frayed denims. Her taste tends to the more exotic.'

'Like Chanel perfume, and outfits by Armani and Gaultier? Is that what turns you on?'

A glinting flame sparked in the depths of his eyes. 'Janet Reger, perhaps. Why the sudden interest, Cassie?'

The softly voiced question sent a swift rush of heat to faintly colour her cheekbones. Denial followed hot on its heels.

'Interest? Me? You have to be joking. I'm merely wondering why you have such a marked antipathy to my presence here. Of course, I didn't realise my clothing would become an issue. I guess that's just one more black mark you have against me. Neither denim nor cotton lace could possibly meet your prerequisites, could they?'

His eyes raked her slowly. The nape of her neck prickled with awareness as she felt his amber gaze shift in gleaming assessment over her slender length.

'Couldn't they?'

She stared at him, wide-eyed, pushing her fingers through the silky cascade of her hair, and his lips twisted in a half-smile, his glance following the unconsciously sensuous movement of her hand.

'Why don't we put an end to this senseless arguing, and find a more pleasurable way of passing the time?' He reached for her, his hands shaping the smooth curve of her hips and drawing her towards him. 'We're quite alone; there's no one to disturb us.' His thumbs began to make slow, circling movements that burned into her flesh, even through the taut constriction of her shorts. A gleam lit his eyes, devilment lurking there, and, with a start, she came out of the hypnotic trance he had lulled her into.

'N-no,' she yelped, jumping back, away from him. He was teasing her, making fun of her, and she had almost fallen for it. 'You're just trying to sway me off course,' she muttered, 'so that you can go home telling yourself how useless I am, and how like a woman to let herself get side-tracked. Only you're wrong. It won't work. I'm going to do this properly. I have to go now; I have things to do.'

'That goes for both of us,' he said, casting a thoughtful glance around. 'There's still some fencing I have to fix in place, so I'll leave you to get on. With nightfall drawing close, you'll have a lot to see to. The temperature will probably drop quite drastically from now on—but I dare say once you have your shelter constructed you'll get by well enough.' Amusement glimmered in his eyes. 'You could always light a fire near-by, too—that might serve to keep any stray animals away.'

She repressed a shudder. He was trying to frighten her, make her show her weakness so that he could laugh in her face, but she wouldn't give him the satisfaction.

'Thanks for the advice,' she said, stiffening her shoulders. 'Don't let me keep you.' What kinds of animals did he mean? She frowned. He was making it up. There weren't any really dangerous animals in this part of the country. Were there? Of course he was making it up. She wouldn't let it bother her. Anyway, it was just as well she had stuffed some matches into her holdall. They were bound to come in useful.

She set off for the copse. The wind was getting up, but the small clearing seemed an ideal place to set up home for the night. She hoped the grey, cloud-laden sky didn't mean trouble. She pushed the thought aside. Large, leafy branches were what she needed. She'd soon have a shelter made up. Pity she hadn't been able to bring a tent along, but she'd had to travel light in the hope that Ryker wouldn't discover her.

A hack-saw would have come in handy to use on the branches, but she made do with her bare hands, breaking off what she needed, and sending her silent apologies to the maimed trees. The dry timber from the ground would serve for the fire.

He was leaning against a tree trunk as she came back into the clearing with her load. The wind buffeted her, making the task of dragging her burden more difficult. 'I thought you had pressing work to do,' she enquired coolly.

'It'll keep for a while.' He folded his arms across his broad chest. 'This promises to be far more interesting than what I had in mind.' There was glinting mockery in the way his eyes appraised her. He wanted her to make a mess of it. He was just waiting to see her fail dismally.

She ground her teeth together as she ransacked her holdall for a length of twine, scattering supplies in all directions as the fading light hampered her search. At last she found it. Knotting the branches together, she heaved them into position, her breathing laboured as she braced the overhanging boughs to form a makeshift roof. That done, she stood back and contemplated the result.

Ryker was still there, she noticed uncomfortably, his narrowed gaze shifting over her handiwork. What was he thinking? His shuttered expression told her nothing. Her fingers twisted in the belt of her shorts. She *had* remembered everything he'd told her all those years ago, hadn't she? She had listened avidly to everything he'd had to say. She had wanted to know everything there was to know about him, and now...he didn't want her anywhere near him. Her throat closed painfully on the thought.

Lord, she could do with a coffee. At least she wasn't cold now, after all that activity, but her shirt felt damp, and she realised with something of a shock that it had started to rain, and the wind was driving it her way.

'Presumably you have your shelter already made,' she said, bothered by his continuing presence. 'Why don't you go and use it?' She slammed the lid down on the treacherous hope that he might want to stay with her. 'I've no inclination to let you share mine.'

'Just as well, then, that I won't be asking. It looks as though it might be a bit cramped in there, anyway. Besides——' he glanced up at the dark, gloom-ridden sky '—I'm not altogether convinced that it would last long enough to see us through till morning.'

She threw him a sharp, questioning look. 'What's wrong with it? Why shouldn't it last? I've tied everything together.'

'So you have.'

When he made no further comment, she decided to ignore him. Holding down her flyaway curls, she dived for cover from the blustering gale and fished out her matches from her bag. He probably expected her to rub two sticks together to make a fire, but she had to draw the line somewhere. She'd already regretfully consigned the small Primus stove to the back of a cupboard at her flat. Coffee, though, she could not bring herself to do without.

With water from the canister, she could be enjoying a hot drink within minutes. If the smell of coffee tormented him and made him think what he was missing, that was just too bad; he could go and get his own. He was standing there, watching her every move, and making it perfectly clear he had no intention of helping her out. She lit the dry wood as another gust of wind hit her sanctum and the whole edifice seemed to sway. Carefully, she placed a pan of water over the flames.

Spooning sugar into her mug, she told herself Ryker could not possibly have done any better. Heavens, there was a storm blowing out there; it was bound to shift a little. Frowning, she tugged the damp shirt away from her skin, listening to the loud creaks and whines as the wind tore with mischievous fingers at her flimsy refuge. Another blast, and there was an ominous, sharp crack.

Cassie watched in choked disbelief as the pan tipped over, and the orange glow of the fire guttered and died as water doused the flames. The sound of splintering wood followed, and she cursed vehemently as the whole structure slowly collapsed on top of her.

Humiliatingly, Ryker pulled her out from the tangle of branches. His grin added to her mortification, and she slapped his hands away. 'Go away,' she said, her voice fraught. 'I don't need you. You wouldn't have done any better.'

His mouth curved wider. 'Maybe not.'

She sent him a black scowl. 'I told you before; don't you dare laugh at me.'

'As if I would.' Unholy light danced in his eyes, and her scowl deepened.

'The wood's too thin and weak,' she gritted, tugging twigs from her hair and flinging them to the ground. 'That's the problem.' He carried a saw and hammer and nails with him, didn't he? Was that what made up the thinking man's survival kit these days? Pity she hadn't had room in her bag. 'Those knots I tied were perfect; I know they were. They'd stand up to anything.'

He was still grinning, the fiend. 'Except a westerly wind. I imagine you'd have fared better over on the east side of the island.'

A dark glower shaded the twin spots of colour that burned high in her cheeks. Why hadn't she taken that into account? Of course he was right.

A low, ominous rumble of thunder sounded in the distance, and she hid a grimace. 'Don't imagine I shall let a little thing like a puff of wind throw me,' she told him. She searched the wreckage for what she could salvage, seizing on a gnarled branch. 'This is just a minor set-back,' she said, brandishing the wood like a sword in front of her. 'It isn't going to knock me off my feet.' She jumped as a streak of lightning raced across the sky. Rain hissed over the ground, plastering her clothes to her skin.

'Put the wood down,' he said, 'before it does one of us some damage.'

She viewed him abstractedly, her attention caught by another crash of thunder. The roar of blood thrummed in her ears.

Ryker bent down and retrieved her belongings from the jumble of wood on the ground.

'I have to start again,' she muttered, frowning as he straightened and purposefully removed the branch from her clenched fingers.

'No, you don't,' he said peremptorily. 'You're coming with me. We'll spend the night on my side of the island. You're getting soaked, and I don't want a case of pneumonia on my hands on top of everything else.'

'Oh, thanks; thanks a lot for that deep, heartfelt consideration,' she gritted, setting her teeth. 'But I really wouldn't like to put you to that trouble. I shall stay here and sort myself out, and if I should, by any remote chance, contract some deadly disease, I'll endeavour to expire quietly, with the minimum of fuss. Please go away, Ryker. I can manage perfectly well on my own.'

Another blinding fork of lightning seemed to split the sky in two. 'That's as may be,' Ryker said, taking her arm in a firm grip, and swinging her holdall over his shoulder. 'But I'm not prepared to take the risk. You'll spend the night with me, and if that idea doesn't appeal that's hard luck. I'm in no mood for argument. Are you coming under your own steam, or do I carry you?'

The pressure on her arm increased. 'There's no need to pull,' she said darkly. How could she refuse such a gracious invitation? He was really looking forward to her company, wasn't he? 'I know you're stronger than I am. You don't have to prove it.'

'Then get a move on.'

They walked through meadowland and across rugged outcrops of rock, heading east. At last Ryker said, 'Here we are. We can get in out of the rain and dry out a bit.'

She stood very still, and stared. 'It's a hut,' she said thickly. 'Ryker... it's a hut.' She was completely nonplussed. It was the last thing she had expected to see. 'You cheated.' Her voice rose in an outburst of disbelief. 'It's a purpose-built cabin. It was here all the time.' She sent him an accusing look. 'I thought this was supposed to be all about survival?'

'I'm not here to pit my wits against the elements,' he told her raspingly. 'I came here to do a job—to prepare the groundwork—and I shall be leaving first thing in the morning.'

He pushed open the door of the cabin and went inside. 'Once I get the fire going,' he said, as she followed him into the room, 'it will soon start to warm up in here. Take off your wet things and grab a couple of blankets from the shelf.'

Cassie's eyes widened as he went over to a wood-burning stove that stood in one corner. He started a small blaze. 'Hurry up,' he said, eyeing her wet clothes with disfavour. 'You're dripping all over the floor.'

She stared around. There was a table, solid and serviceable, a camp-bed with a sleeping-bag thrown over it, and a couple of chairs. The shelves were stacked with provisions of all kinds.

His voice sounded warningly in her ears, and she jumped again. 'If I start to hear your teeth chattering, I shall take matters into my own hands. Put your things to dry near the fire.'

He started to strip off his own shirt, and she caught a stunning glimpse of his deeply tanned male torso. He was magnificent to look at, lean and tautly muscled, his skin gleaming faintly gold in a way that tugged at her senses. She felt an aching need to touch him.

Shakily, she turned away, and reached for a woollen blanket to cover herself while she undressed. He had no such qualms, it seemed. He'd have taken everything off, whether or not she had continued to stare. Hurriedly, she dealt with her garments, wrapping herself in the voluminous folds of soft wool.

'Soup, I think,' he said, and she sent him a covert glance, relieved to find that he had donned a fresh pair of jeans and a cream sweater. All her clothes had suffered in the storm raging outside. The holdall had developed a leak.

She sighed. 'Does it have to be nettle soup?' she queried tentatively. 'I think I may develop an allergy.'

He grinned. 'I can probably come up with something better than that. Hot, thick vegetable, with fresh, crusty rolls. How does that sound?'

'Wonderful.' She sent him a smoky glance. 'You're a fiend; you know that, don't you?'

He laughed. 'You were the one who wanted to fend for yourself in primitive surroundings. Who am I to stop you?'

When the soup was piping hot, and she had fixed a pot of coffee, they sat down at the scrubbed wooden table. Cassie said, 'You never did tell me what it was that made you set up these centres.'

'Didn't I?' He applied himself to his soup.

She wondered if he was reluctant to talk about it. 'It's strange, isn't it,' she said, 'that people should be interested in learning how to cope in the wild? I suppose, in a way, it's exchanging the tensions of the concrete jungle for a challenge of another kind.' Breaking off a chunk of bread, she studied him thoughtfully. 'You were doing it for real in the beginning, weren't you? When you were in the Army. I should have thought...' She paused, uncertain, then plunged on. 'After the way your father went missing, I should have thought survival techniques were the last thing you wanted to get into. Didn't it bring back awful memories? You must have been only a child when it happened.'

He did not answer for a moment, and she began to regret her hastily posed questions. Then he said quietly, 'It always haunted me, not knowing what had happened to him after his plane crashed. Although he and his friend had managed to get clear of the wreckage, there was no trace of what happened to them.'

'But surely there must have been something, some clue?'

He shook his head. 'They had registered a flight plan in the usual way, but by the time it was realised something had happened conditions had deteriorated on the mountains. Temperatures were way below freezing, and a blizzard sprang up. There was no chance of finding them.'

'Ryker, I'm so sorry.' She reached out and touched his hand briefly.

'It all happened a long time ago,' he said.

She was silent for a moment, then said quietly, 'Your mother took the news very badly, didn't she?'

'I watched her give up hope and gradually fade away. They said it was heart failure. I was angry. Why hadn't he survived? Why didn't he get back to us?'

'Is that why you joined the Army?'

He finished off his coffee. 'I had no family left, so it seemed a natural choice of career. After a while, I realised that there was something I could do during my stint in the services, something that might give more than the ghost of a chance to some unlucky soul who crash-lands in a war zone, or goes astray in unknown territory. So I specialised in training recruits in those skills for a time. It wasn't much of a compensation for my own loss, but at least it helped me keep my sanity.'

Cassie said nothing, acknowledging the deep sorrow he must have felt at losing both parents, the strength he had dragged from within himself to fight back.

'Life goes on,' he said. 'You learn that there are other challenges to meet, different mountains to conquer.'

'So when you left the Army,' she mused, 'you used the skills you had learned to set up the centres?'

'It seemed the logical thing to do at the time. And it helped to fund the charter business later. I don't have a great deal to do with the pursuits centres these days, but I enjoy overseeing them occasionally, or looking out new locations such as this.'

'Have you finished everything that you came here to do? You said you were leaving tomorrow.'

He nodded. 'Mostly. All the dangerous areas are fenced off now, so we can leave first thing in the morning. I've meetings scheduled on the mainland, so I have to get back as soon as possible.'

They would go back, she thought bleakly, and he would once more move out of her life. A shiver ran through her and she pulled the blanket more firmly around herself.

'You're still cold,' Ryker said. His gaze rested on her, and she wondered what it was that she could see in his eyes. Was it concern, affection even? Perhaps he did care for her, just a little. Perhaps—hope darted fitfully—more than just a little... Was it possible?

Ryker stood up, saying briskly, 'Come over to the stove and get warmed up.'

She stretched wearily, and walked towards the heater as he had suggested. Despite the hot soup and the growing warmth of the room, the cold seemed to have seeped into her bones. The cold of loneliness . . .

Unexpectedly, Ryker's arms came around her, hugging her close, his hands chafing warmth into her arms, sliding along her back. 'You should have said you were still feeling chilled,' he admonished her.

The touch of his hands, the pressuring warmth, was almost too much for her. She wished that this closeness meant more to him, that he would hold her as though that was where she belonged, with him for a lifetime. But how could that ever be, when there was Sophie . . . ?

Her head dropped, her cheek resting against the solid warmth of his shoulder, taking what comfort she could from his nearness. Sophie was not here, and Ryker's arms were holding her safe. She would keep that thought next to her heart and cherish it.

'You're tired,' he said. 'It's been a long day, one way and another.' He moved away from her, and she felt the sudden sharp pang of loss. 'You'd better use this for tonight,' he said, unzipping the sleeping-bag. 'It's only a narrow camp-bed, but you should be fairly comfortable.'

'But what will you do?' She glanced around. 'I don't like to mess up your arrangements.'

'I'll put some blankets on the floor. It's no problem. Now, get some sleep. We need to make an early start tomorrow.'

CHAPTER SIX

RYKER said little to Cassie next morning, concentrating instead on loading supplies on to the launch, and making ready for the journey back to the mainland. Studying his broad back as she tried to help, Cassie wondered if, in the light of day, he felt a renewed surge of anger because she had gone against his wishes in going to the island. His manner seemed distant, and she was not sure whether it was purely due to his preoccupation with other matters.

'Leave that,' he ordered briskly, as she made to haul a box on deck. 'Perhaps you could see to a pot of coffee before we set off?'

Feeling that she was somehow in the way, she did as he suggested. While she waited for the water to boil, she picked up her notebook and scribbled a few hurried lines. Coming back into the cabin, Ryker sent her a steel-eyed glance that made her falter. Hastily, she pushed the book back into her holdall. She had no wish to do anything which would bring an end to the brief moments of closeness they had shared. The glowing memory of being in his arms was something she wanted to hold on to for a while longer.

Reality, though, intruded all too soon. 'Where do you want me to drop you?' he said as they drove into the city some hours later. 'Are you going straight back to the flat?'

She checked her watch. 'I think I'd better call in at the office. There are one or two leads I have to follow up, and I can probably make a start this afternoon.'

The interview she pursued took longer than she had estimated, and by the time she had written up the piece it was very late. As she eased her tense limbs, it dawned on her that she had missed out on a meal, and when a few of her colleagues voted on a hot snack at the local pub it seemed like a good idea. The prospect of going back to her flat, when Ryker would not be there, was dismal, and she made an effort, instead, to join in with the banter going on around her.

When she eventually made it back to her apartment, she was too tired to do more than scrub herself clean and fling herself into bed. Last night seemed so far away now, and she closed her eyes on thoughts of Ryker, wishing he were still with her.

Morning came too soon. Slipping her silk robe over her underwear, Cassie emerged from the bathroom with a weary yawn. At least the shower had gone part way to refreshing her. She would get to grips with some writing as soon as she had eaten. Producing something on the pursuits centre would take careful thought, if Ryker was to approve. Not that there would have been any problem if Jim didn't constantly try to add his own slant.

'You're scowling,' Nick said, startling her as she walked into the kitchen. 'What brought that on?'

She looked at him, her mind disorientated for a moment or two. Puzzled, she said, 'Nick? What are you doing here?'

'You asked me to keep an eye on the place while the builders finished off, remember?' He grinned. 'It was only a few days ago; you can't have forgotten?'

'No, but——'

'They were working until late, and it took me a couple of hours to tidy up after them, so I decided I might as well stay over in your spare room—I didn't think you'd mind.'

She shook her head. 'No, of course not. I'm sorry, I don't seem to be thinking too clearly this morning. Thanks for straightening things up, though you should have left it for me. I'd have seen to it.'

'It was no trouble.' He gave her a speculative look. 'Why don't you put me out of my misery, and marry me? We go back a long way, don't we? We share the same interests—couldn't we make a go of it?'

Cassie's blue eyes clouded. 'I wish I could tell you what you want to hear, Nick. I'm sorry. I *do* like you. I've always thought of you as my friend, but I can't give you more than that.'

'It's Ryker, isn't it?' There was a bitterness in his voice. 'If he wasn't on the scene I'd be in with a chance, but ever since he came back you've been different; you've been edgy the whole time.'

'Have I? I don't know. I'm very confused about everything just now.'

'There's no future for you with him. He already has a relationship, with his secretary. Forget him, Cassie. I can make you happy.'

'Please, Nick, don't push it,' she said, her throat tight. 'I've told you before; I don't want to talk about him, and I'm not going to argue with you.' She went over to the percolator and spooned in fresh coffee.

Seeing her closed features, he bit back what he was about to say. 'OK,' he said, resignedly. 'Have it your way for now. But I shan't give up. Perhaps we can talk about this again later.' He appeared harassed. 'Right now, I have to go out on a job; there's just time for a quick shave.' He started towards the bathroom. 'Your father rang, by the way. He's been trying to reach you for some time.'

'What did he want?'

Nick shrugged. 'He didn't say, but he didn't sound in a very good mood.'

The doorbell rang as he disappeared into the bathroom, and Cassie frowned. She only hoped it wasn't her father come to take her to task. She wasn't up to dealing with him right now, not before breakfast.

It was Ryker. Seeing him standing there outside her door, large as life and twice as overpowering, made her heart leap.

'Ryker,' she murmured, staring at him, drinking in his familiar, bone-meltingly attractive features.

'Are you going to keep me standing out here all day?' he asked quizzically. 'I thought I might at least get a foot in the door.'

'Oh!' Slowly, her faculties returned. 'Of course, you want to come in.' She stood to one side, toying with the belt of her robe.

He looked at her oddly, his brows pulled together in a slight frown, and walked through to the lounge. Removing his grey leather jacket, he threw it over the settee and remarked thoughtfully, 'I take it the builders have finished now?'

She nodded, her eyes drawn to the breadth of his shoulders, his long, lean frame.

'Is something wrong, Cassie?' he murmured. 'You look a little distracted this morning.' He began to wander around her living-room, glancing over her bookshelves. He removed a paperback and flicked lightly through it.

'No.' She found her voice. 'I just hadn't been expecting you, that's all. I mean, you didn't say you'd call. I thought...' She stumbled to a halt as Nick walked into the room.

'You're about out of toothpaste,' he said. 'Shall I——? Oh...' He stopped short as he saw Ryker.

Ryker's stare was deadly, his eyes narrowing on a dangerous glitter as he looked from one to the other. Nick paled slightly under his tan.

'Now I see,' Ryker said, his voice grating in the silence that descended, 'why you were so put out by my arrival.' Throwing the book to one side, he went on, 'You didn't tell me I was interrupting something.' His face might have been chiselled from a block of ice, and Cassie braced herself against the involuntary shiver that coursed along her spine.

She said quietly, 'I think you might be jumping to conclusions, Ryker.'

'Really?' His gaze streaked over her with cold insolence, and she was tautly conscious that the flimsy robe did little to conceal her feminine curves from his roving scrutiny. 'I shouldn't have thought there was much room for ambiguity, would you?'

Nick's mouth twisted. 'Cassie doesn't need your approval or disapproval, Ryker. She's free to do whatever she wants. It's entirely her choice if she wants to share her roof with a man. I doubt very much that you consult her when you invite a woman to stay with you.'

Cassie felt sick. She did not want to think about Ryker and other women.

'If I want your opinion,' Ryker said, his jaw clenching, 'I'll let you know.'

Nick's eyes flickered slightly, and he turned to Cassie. 'Look, I have to go; I'm late already. I'll bring a few supplies back with me. You seem to be running short of one or two things.'

Cassie frowned darkly as the door closed behind him. Nick had done it deliberately—thrown down a casual remark designed to mislead, almost as though he was staking a claim. Sooner or later, they would have to have a long, serious talk.

She breathed deeply. Even though she disliked his way of tackling things, Nick did have a point. What right did Ryker have to sneer, when Sophie shared his bed? That she did so, Cassie was in no doubt. Ryker was too male to be satisfied with a platonic relationship.

'What's got into you?' Ryker demanded. A muscle flicked jerkily at the side of his mouth. 'Have you taken leave of your senses? Don't you know any better than to throw in your lot with that unscrupulous snapshot merchant?'

'Is he any worse than you?' she flung back. 'You're the last one who should be throwing stones. At least Nick treats me with tenderness and respect. He doesn't try to drop me down cliffs.'

'No,' he agreed savagely, leashed violence in his glittering stare. 'He spends all his time bedding you, doesn't he? Is that what turns you on, making out with the paparazzi?'

She gasped at the insult, the blood draining from her face, and he studied her with measured contempt. 'No wonder you're in such a scratchy mood most of the time. Too many late nights.'

'You are despicable,' she said, lacing each word with acid distaste. 'And my disposition might improve by leaps and bounds if I were to find that this was all a bad dream, that your presence here is purely a figment of my imagination. As it is, I don't have to put up with you or your nasty remarks any longer. You know where the door is—I suggest that you use it.'

'I'm not ready to go yet.'

His cold arrogance fuelled her temper. 'Aren't you? Why exactly did you come here today, Ryker? It can't only have been that you wanted to throw insults at me.'

'I came,' he said curtly, 'to look over the article you're planning.'

'I don't work with people breathing over my shoulder,' she informed him frigidly.

'Even better. Consigning the whole thing to perdition is more or less what I had in mind, anyway.'

'Then it's fortunate you don't have a say in what I choose to do. If, and when, I produce an article bearing some reference to you, I'll allow you the privilege of reading through it before I commit it to print. Until that time comes, there's little point in your idling around here. I'd appreciate it if you would go.'

He ignored her blatant hostility. 'How long has he been staying here?'

Her skin prickled with annoyance. 'That's none of your business.'

'I'm making it mine. He's no good. It's time you realised that his attitude to you is tempered by what he hopes to gain long-term. He might well be interested in you as a woman, but the fact that one day you're going to be very wealthy weighs heavily in his scheme.'

'Are you still on that tack? Why don't you give it a rest, Ryker? You've told me what you think, and I've duly filed it. My eyes are wide open, and I'm quite happy with things the way they are. I don't see any need for you to keep emphasising the point.'

'I disagree. Since I don't believe you have fully appreciated the message yet, perhaps I should drive it home a little harder. Nick isn't the one for you.

How can he be, when you return another man's kisses with such sweet enthusiasm?'

He came towards her, and, too late, she read the intent that flamed in his eyes. She swallowed. 'Ryker, you——'

'That's right, Cassie. Me. You melt so delightfully whenever you're in my arms. I think it's time we explored that intriguing fact, don't you?'

He reached for her, and she began to struggle, trying to twist away from the restricting pressure of his hands, her robe caught up by the solid weight of his thigh, her wrist clamped in his large fingers.

'Let me go, Ryker,' she said urgently, fearful of the betraying pulse of her senses, her body's treacherous response whenever he was near.

He laughed softly, a breath of sound in the back of his throat. 'I think not.'

His glance shimmered over her, taking in the tangle of silk, the smooth expanse of her naked shoulder laid bare to his gaze. 'How do you account for the way you tremble in my arms, Cassie, if he means so much to you?'

His mouth covered hers, crushing the softness of her lips with bruising intensity. She was swamped by a wave of dizziness that left her weak, her limbs without substance. A shuddery sigh racked her body, and he bound her closer to him, wrapping her firmly in the circle of his arms. The lazy flick of his tongue slowly undermined her resolve, laid waste her will-power to push him away, reminded her of all the honeyed dreams she had woven around the two of them.

As his hands caressed her, stroking along her spine, sweet, thrilling sensation unfurled inside her, and she yielded restlessly to the sensuous demand, leaning into him, returning his kiss with heated, tremulous passion. Her fingers shook, trailing lightly over his neck, absently seeking out the strong column of his throat.

A low moan escaped her, muffled by the slow glide of his mouth as it drifted down to explore the loosened edges of her robe. Fleetingly, his tongue ran over the smooth creamy expanse of her shoulder, pausing to nuzzle the line of her collarbone, and the scalloped, lacy edge of her bra. Then, shockingly, he dipped his head to brush his lips over the throbbing, turgid mound of her breast. A soft, shuddery cry broke in her throat, her fingertips gripping convulsively into the fine fabric of his shirt. He moved, shifting his weight slightly to angle her against the rigid support of a cupboard, his hands stroking the rounded curve of her hips, drawing her to him so that she could feel the hard, raw urgency of his desire.

'How can you deny the way you feel?' he muttered roughly. 'There's no mistaking the soft, supple invitation of your body.' The warmth of his mouth on her throat brought heated tremors to course through her limbs. 'You want me. I could take you here and now,' he said huskily, 'I could lose myself in you.'

Her untutored body quivered in response, whispers of caution swamped by her own need, by her recognition that this was the man she loved, had waited for, craved for so many years that she could not bear to turn him away.

'Ryker...' She looked into his eyes, wanting his words of love, desperately longing for some sign that his feelings went as deep as her own, but her thoughts turned quickly to despair. What she read in his smouldering gaze was not love; it was pure desire, a hot, swift, demanding passion, a raging fire that would consume her and leave her shattered in its wake.

The long, shrill cry of her broken dreams sounded a jarring note in her head, echoed in some far distant place like a peal of bells. Slowly the ringing of the phone pierced her consciousness, and she heard Ryker mutter a low curse. 'You'd better answer it,' he said.

Bemused, she straightened her robe and ran a hand shakily through her hair. She swallowed, and breathed deeply several times before she could bring herself to cut off that relentless, urgent demand.

James Wyatt's voice was edged with frost. 'So I've managed to track you down at last. First you're in that wretched squat, living in a commune, your photo splashed all over the papers. If it hadn't been for Ryker arranging that new accommodation, Lord knows what would have happened. The family name would have been dragged right through the mud. I'm warning you, Cassandra, it's time this nonsense came to an end.'

He paused briefly. 'There's a job in the company open for you. There has been all along. You can start next month and we'll forget what's gone before, but if you choose to defy me I'll think again about your trust fund, and you can say goodbye to your inheritance.'

Cassie held the receiver away from her, and closed her eyes briefly as though it would in some way shut off the flow of words.

'And where have you been these last few days? Chasing halfway across the country on some fool errand, no doubt.'

'I was with Ryker,' she said. 'There was no need for you to worry.'

'Where is he now?'

'He's here.'

'Put him on; I want to talk to him. I've an important business meeting coming up in a few weeks. I need him to fly me up there. The fewer people who know about it the better.'

She handed the phone to Ryker and sat down on the couch, pulling her robe protectively around herself.

Ryker's tone was even and unperturbed, as though nothing had happened between them, as though what had been momentous to her had not even begun to ruffle the calm surface of his demeanour. He had switched off, just as quickly as if he had snapped his fingers.

How could she even have hoped that he might have some spark of feeling for her? The only reason he had made love to her at all was because he wanted to prove a point.

Ryker finished the call and looked across at her, his dark brow raised in question. 'What was all that about?'

His cool, detached manner helped to restore function to her brain once more. She sighed. 'I'm disinherited again,' she said, her mouth twisting in a rueful curve. 'He's never liked my working as a journalist. My being at the squat was the final straw.'

'Can you blame him?'

She considered him impassively. 'It's all in the past now. It won't serve anything to rake over old embers. Though I'd quite like to submit a final piece to add to the feature I wrote. Your friend, the one who supplied the accommodation, would make a likely candidate for an interview, don't you agree? It would round off the whole series of articles quite nicely.'

'Gregson?' He absorbed the cool blue challenge of her gaze. 'I dare say something could be fixed up. It would mean your coming along to the annual gathering on Saturday. He promised he'd be there.'

Her brows lifted. 'You astonish me. Isn't this an about-turn? Don't you have any objections to throw at me? I'm not used to your conceding ground so easily.'

'Somehow,' he said drily, 'I have the feeling that a refusal would make very little difference. On current showing, you'd turn up anyway.' He came over to the couch, and sat down beside her, his amber gaze shifting over her, taking in her tense form, the jutting angle of her jaw.

She registered his nearness with a darkly brooding resentment. Did he think she would be gullible enough to fall into his arms a second time that day?

She studied the hard, strong-boned lines of his face, the firm mouth that had only a short time ago wreaked such devastating havoc on her senses. Pain knotted inside her, and abruptly she thrust the hurtful thoughts away, closing her mind against the harsh imagery. Why had she deluded herself that there could ever be anything between her and Ryker? He was only here because of the article she meant to write, and now she had blown everything, made a fatal mistake. She had shown him that she could be vulnerable to his lovemaking. She had to bring things back on to an even keel.

Her lashes flickered, hiding her dark abstraction. 'As you offered so generously, I accept. I'll drive down to your place on Saturday.' She paused. 'I take it that Sophie will be there?'

Ryker hesitated, his eyes narrowing on her. 'She said she would try to make it. Why? Is that a problem?'

'Not at all,' she said, her voice faintly distant. 'But if most people are going as couples, I hope you won't have any objections if I bring someone along with me.'

'Who did you have in mind? Driscoll?' His mouth made a hard line, his eyes taking on the glitter of tempered steel. 'Why should I let——?'

'I know you don't like him,' Cassie interrupted coolly. 'You've made that quite plain on more than one occasion, but if I'm to conduct an interview I want photos too. Nick works with me. I need him to come along.'

He viewed her thoughtfully for a long moment. 'Why do I get the impression that I'm being manoeuvred?'

'Do you, Ryker?' she murmured with feigned sympathy. 'Now who's being uptight, I wonder? You really should learn to take things at face value once in a while. All this suspicion must be very wearisome. Why don't you think of it as the chance for both of you to air your feelings? I'm sure you can be civilised about it, both being grown men.' There was a hint of mischief in her tone. 'Or is that too much to ask?'

'Let me warn you, Cassie,' he said roughly, 'if there's any trouble, if he uses that camera of his to angle after a centre-page spread of my guests, he'll find himself out on the pavement.'

'I can well imagine it,' she said drily. 'Would that apply to me, too?'

His smile was brief and humourless. 'Oh, I think not, my sweet. I'm sure there are other, far more satisfying ways of dealing with you.' He paused, speculation in his prowling gaze, and she knew a vague flicker of unease. His mind was busy ticking over, and it didn't bode well for her, that was for sure. His expression held all the lethal promise of a ruthless predator.

'Ryker——' she began, but he cut her off.

'Bring him along, by all means. I have the feeling that, one way and another, Saturday could prove to be quite an interesting day.'

CHAPTER SEVEN

CASSIE pressed her finger to the doorbell, and listened as the chimes echoed faintly through the corridors of the big house, their resonance muted by the sound of music and laughter.

'He must have quite a crowd in there,' Nick said, a faint smile playing over his mouth. 'I wonder if Hal Gregson's arrived yet, and had time to mellow?'

His grey eyes silvered in the moonlight and Cassie said sharply, 'You're here to take one or two photos of him, if he gives permission. Other than that, you keep the cover firmly on the lens, is that clear? This is supposed to be a social gathering, not a news stunt.'

'Of course,' he murmured, his voice amused. 'I know that. Don't worry so much; I won't let you down.'

Her brows pulled together in a frown. 'I thought we'd mix a little, that's all—get to know a few people, make contacts, nothing more.'

'I understand that,' Nick agreed, sliding a hand around her waist. 'Relax. I reckon this could turn out to be a great idea of yours.'

Cassie wasn't so sure. She had started to have doubts about the whole thing, from the moment Ryker had been in agreement. Why had he had such a sudden change of heart, been quite happy to have

Nick come as her partner? He was planning something, she was certain of it, and now she couldn't
think why she had been foolish enough to push it
in the first place.

She could always have persuaded Hal Gregson
into an interview by phoning him up in office hours.
OK, so it was good to meet someone socially, and
it might help to get her off to a better start, but
that wasn't the real reason she was here, was it?
Hadn't she, in some dark, perverse corner of her
mind, wanted desperately to see Ryker again,
grasped at the merest chance of a meeting? Even
knowing how little he cared, some tormentor inside
her had prodded her into accepting this invitation,
some masochistic instinct had pushed her into this
act of folly.

It was too late to be having second thoughts. The
door opened, and her nervous system sent out a red
alert as Ryker came into her line of vision.

'Cassie...come on in.' He nodded briefly to Nick,
then stood back as they walked into the hall, his
gaze travelling slowly over her. Then he smiled, a
devastating, attractive smile that did something
wonderful to his features and sent her lungs into a
spasm of shock. All at once she was finding it difficult to breathe; her mouth was dry as dust.

He looked different, somehow. Maybe it was the
suit that did it, dove-grey, the expensive tailoring
sitting well on his broad shoulders, his cream silk
shirt contrasting with the bronze of his throat, the
grey trousers emphasising the taut, muscular
strength of his legs. Or maybe it was the spark that

glimmered briefly in his eyes that had disturbed her.
It was the look of the hunter, she registered in
growing alarm, the stealthy satisfaction of one who
knew that the snare was laid, the trap was set. She
moistened her lips with the tip of her tongue and
tried to pull herself together. She was being fan-
ciful. Looks could be deceptive.

Leading them through to the main lounge, Ryker
furnished them both with a drink, and said
thoughtfully, 'I expect you'd like me to introduce
you to one or two people.' He sent a searching
glance around the room, and Cassie gulped down
the sparkling wine, savouring the cool liquid as it
slid down her parched throat.

She watched with suspicion as Ryker took Nick
to one side, saying smoothly, 'I'm sure you'd like
to meet Marie Delahaie. You two have something
in common, since she's extremely interested in photography, though not as a professional.'

Marie Delahaie's eyes lit warmly as she greeted
Nick. She looked as though she had stepped directly from the pages of an *haute couture* magazine,
Cassie thought, looking with admiration at the
classic lines of her dress and jacket. The discreet
gold jewellery she wore at her throat and wrist
spelled out wealth and good taste.

'And you'd like to speak to Hal, wouldn't you,
Cassie?' Ryker murmured, coming back to her. 'I
told him that you'd be here this evening, and he's
looking forward to meeting you. I think we'll find
him in the study, talking to Ray.' Cassie gave her
glass to a passing waiter, and Ryker guided her away

from the crowded room, his hand firmly at her elbow.

'Ray's one of your board members, isn't he?' she queried, trying desperately to ignore the slow burn of his fingers on her bare skin.

'That's right. He's working out a contract for a new administrative centre with Hal, but neither of them will mind if you interrupt them. And if you don't get your business finished this evening, you can always have another word with him in the morning. He'll be staying here overnight.'

'I shan't be here. I'm going back to London later this evening.'

'Nonsense,' he said briskly. 'I know James is away for the night, and you wouldn't want to stay over in the Manor while it's empty, but I'm sure I can find room for you here. Plenty of other people are staying over, and you don't have to let your evening be spoiled by the thought of the journey back. Besides, you came in Nick's car, didn't you? Is yours in the garage again?' His mouth indented fractionally when she didn't reply. 'Anyway, I shouldn't imagine he'll be in any condition to drive in a few hours' time.'

There was probably some truth in that. Although they had agreed on returning home the same day, Nick had already been giving out hints that he wouldn't mind looking out a hotel for the night. Cassie did not want to do that, and Nick had posed her with a problem, since she wasn't sure her money would stretch to alternative travel for the distance home. She was still paying for the renovations to her flat. Even so... 'I don't think I can stay here,' she said.

Ryker came to a halt outside the door of the study, and turned her to him, his hands resting lightly on her arms. She looked at him, a question in her troubled gaze, and he said with a wry inflexion, 'Do you have to make a fight out of everything I say and do? It's no big deal staying here.' His hand went to the door. 'Go and say hello to Hal. You won't mind if I don't stay around, will you? I really should go and find Sophie.' He moved away.

What had she expected? His relationship with Sophie had lasted through all these years, hadn't it? He was bound to be dancing attendance on her this evening. She had known it, yet still she had fought against the demons of her subconscious. Having him so near... close enough to touch... knowing he belonged with someone else, was the purest agony.

She couldn't go on this way, she realised, breathing deeply. She had an interview to conduct, and she had to appear cool and professional.

Several deep breaths helped. Slowly her pulse settled to a more even rhythm, and she went inside the room, steeling herself not to reveal the chaotic confusion of her emotions to either of the two men who came to their feet as she entered.

When she emerged from the study some three-quarters of an hour later, she had a wealth of information at her fingertips, and her address book was filled with valuable contacts.

It was a good thing she had trained herself to concentrate on the task in hand, she reflected soberly, trying to ease the faint throbbing in her head with the slow, circular motion of her fingers on her temples, because the haunting spectre of Ryker and Sophie might well have been her downfall.

Helping herself to another glass of wine from a silver tray in the lounge, she looked around for Nick, and saw him ensconced in a corner with Marie. He beckoned her over.

'Marie was just telling me about her investment in Barton Development,' Nick said. 'That's the same line your father's in, isn't it, Cassie?'

'That's right.' To Marie she said, 'I doubt you'll go wrong with Bartons as part of your share portfolio.' She sipped at her drink. 'From what I gather, the price is rocketing sky-high at the moment.'

'So I understand.' Marie assessed her shrewdly. 'James Wyatt isn't doing too badly either, is he?'

'An understatement if ever I heard one,' Nick laughed, his grey eyes dancing as he looked at Cassie.

A movement at her side alerted her to Ryker's reappearance. She stiffened. He was not alone. Sophie was very much in evidence, her arm locked into his, her body draped over his side in sensual invitation. Cassie swallowed the rest of her wine, and Marie turned a considering glance in her direction.

'And do you have shares in your father's company?' she asked. 'Do you mind my asking? I expect you have one of these trust clauses that allows you so much at a coming-of-age. That's how it was with me; I had to wait until I was twenty-seven to receive the bulk of my income—an age my father considered mature enough to handle it wisely.'

She grinned at Cassie, inviting a response.

'There was something along those lines,' Cassie murmured.

'Was?'

Nick gave her an odd look, and Ryker said drily, 'There was an unfortunate family argument. Cassie's father disinherited her, so now she's quite on her own in the world with regard to finance, isn't that right, Cassie?'

She slid her wine glass on to a shelf. 'You should know,' she said shortly. 'You were there.'

Sophie's mouth thinned disparagingly. 'It was hardly an unexpected turn of events, was it? You might have known if you carried on the way you were going that James would do something about it. You can't go around living with hippies and expect him to swallow it, especially when he's given you every chance to become part of the family firm.'

Cassie's ears had begun to buzz; a tight band was slowly working its way around her head. 'Don't let it upset you, Sophie,' she murmured. 'It's my problem, but I'm sure I shan't end up sleeping rough and holding out my begging-bowl to passers-by in the street.'

Sophie looked at her with distaste. 'Time will tell,' she said.

She turned to Ryker, her mouth softening.
'Darling, I have to go. Could you possibly take me
back to my flat? I hate to drag you away from your
guests, but it doesn't look as though the taxi I ordered is going to arrive, and I need to pick up a
few things before I go to the station. Would you
mind? At least it will give us a little more time to
talk.'

'It's no problem. Just give me a minute with Ray.
He'll hold the fort while I'm gone.'

'I, too, must make my goodbyes,' Marie said in
an apologetic tone. 'Though I don't know what's
happened to my lift. She's probably gorging herself
at the buffet, and won't want to leave, but I really
do have to go. It's the opening week of my new
bistro, and I must put in an appearance, however
late. You're all very welcome to come along at any
time and help me celebrate.'

'I can give you a lift,' Nick said. 'There's no need
to tear your friend away if she's enjoying herself.
I'm more than happy to take you.'

Marie put an affectionate hand on his shoulder.
'What a charming man you are. How kind. You
must, of course, sample the food and wine at my
place. I insist.' She looked encouragingly towards
Cassie. 'And you too, Cassie. Would you join us?'

'I think not, if you don't mind. I said I might
have another word with Hal later.'

Cassie felt a wave of nausea engulf her as she
watched Ryker move away with Sophie, his hand
lifting in a quick gesture of farewell. The woman

was in firm possession, her lips curved in response to something Ryker was saying.

Left alone, Cassie absently took the wine that a waiter offered. She stared at the buffet laid out on long white linen-covered tables, and the sickness returned, clawing at her stomach. Sophie called to him like a siren, and he went eagerly to her side, a willing victim.

Was that what he had wanted from this evening? Was that what he had planned—to show her that Sophie had prime place in his life, that he regretted the lapse he had made when he kissed Cassie, when he had said how much he wanted her? He had been driven by male need, and now he wanted the memory pushed out of the way, forgotten as though it had never existed.

She began to walk about the room, oblivious to the people who talked and laughed, blind to the couples who swayed contentedly to the music. The stairs were ahead of her, and she took them slowly, holding her wine glass carefully, taking small sips as she went. Her head felt slightly dizzy, as though it did not quite belong to her, and she held on to the oak banister with her free hand, willing herself to go one step at a time.

This was Ryker's home, the place he came back to, the place where he ate and slept and where he had lived almost from the first time she had met him. She wanted to know it, to feel it, to absorb its atmosphere into her bones, to have this one little part of him which was all she would ever have.

Each room was stamped with his refined taste, his love of what was solid and enduring, and she examined each one, drifting through them in succession, running her fingers over polished wood, and the smooth luxury of velvet.

She found herself in a large bedroom, and decided hazily that she had come to the end of the line. The carpet beneath her feet was deep-piled and welcoming, and she slipped off her shoes, feeling the soft wool with her stockinged toes.

Sitting down on the big bed, she drained the last of her wine, the bubbles filling her nostrils, tingling the back of her throat, her head swimming with warm sensation. This was where she wanted to be. This felt right, and she lay back, her hands closing on quilted silk, her mind slowly easing into a black, dreamless void.

'Time to surface, sleepyhead, or the coffee and croissants my housekeeper has prepared will go to waste.'

She blinked, then squeezed her eyes tightly shut against the sunlight that streamed in through the undraped windows. A little hammer was working overtime inside her head; her mouth and throat felt achingly dry.

'Come on,' Ryker said firmly, 'drink up. You might try a couple of aspirin, they'll do wonders for your hangover.'

She squinted at him. 'Hangover?' she said, her voice roughened and thick. 'Who said I had a hangover?' She pressed a hand to her throbbing head, and heard Ryker's low chuckle.

Scowling, she picked up the aspirin from the bedside table and tasted the coffee. It was good. She savoured it slowly, then lay back against the pillows, closing her eyes, her limbs cushioned against the softness of the mattress, the tiredness seeping out of her body.

Some minutes later, she felt his presence by the side of the bed, and she slanted him a look. He wasn't even dressed properly. She blinked again, her blue eyes busy taking in the fact that he wore only dark trousers, and that his chest was bare and his black hair was still damp from the shower.

'Why aren't you in your room, Ryker?' she muttered. 'How can I get up and get dressed with you hovering around?'

He rubbed at his hair with a towel. 'Actually, this *is* my room. It's clear you were in such a state last night that you didn't know whose bed you climbed into. Just as well it was mine. It could have caused problems with some of the guests.' He grinned and she threw him a black look.

'I didn't climb into bed. I just . . .' Her brows met in a frown. What had she done last night? She remembered sitting on the quilt; that was clear enough in her head. The folds of her dress had caught underneath her, and she'd lain back; that had unlocked the ravels of material.

Her shoes were on the carpet where she had left them. She stared at the floor. No, she hadn't pushed them tidily under the chair; she was sure about that.

'Where is my dress?' she muttered. 'I don't recall——'

'I put it on a hanger for you,' Ryker said. 'You wouldn't have wanted it creased, would you?'

'I don't remember...' It dawned on her that, beneath the light covering of the quilt, she was wearing very little. And how had she come to be actually beneath the quilt? She stared at him, her eyes widening, and he returned her look with one of total innocence—feigned innocence, she realised with growing wrath.

'You undressed me,' she accused, a tidal wave of heat invading her from top to toe. 'How could you; how dared you?'

'You were in no state to do it yourself.' He seemed to muse a moment. 'What happened to the cotton lace, by the way? I must say, silk does have a certain quality all of its own. Not that I noticed, of course.'

His mouth began to tilt at the corners, and she aimed the pillow at him. He caught it, and placed it carefully on the end of the bed, and the gleam she saw darting in his eyes incensed her even more.

'Don't stand there tormenting me, you fiend. I didn't mean to stay here in the first place, much less in your bed. Get out of here and leave me alone. Find somebody else to annoy.'

'It's hardly my fault if you were upset by your boyfriend's defection last night, now, is it?'

'Defection?' Her voice thickened.

'Well, call it what you will. I didn't force him to leave, and it wasn't me who encouraged him to stay over at Marie's place. Money, though, does seem to have its own magnetic attraction for him. It must have come as a shock to him to find that you no longer had an inheritance.'

Her mind was working rapidly now. Was that what Ryker had been plotting all along—to get rid of Nick? He must have been instrumental in setting up the whole thing.

'You knew that would happen, didn't you?' she said, her tone becoming acrid. 'That's why you introduced them. How did you know that Marie would play into your hands?'

He shrugged, not bothering to deny it. 'She's a very good friend of mine. When I asked her to help out, she was only too happy to oblige. Like it or not, Cassie, he's no good, and when the time is right he'll find himself given very short shrift by Marie Delahaie.'

'You're quite ruthless, aren't you?' Cassie said bitingly. 'Who asked you to interfere?'

'You're better off without him. You know that, even though you're snapping at me. And he won't be back in your life in quite the same way ever again, Cassie; I hope you accept that. He'll only turn on the charm when he wants something. You may not be happy about it, but that's how it is.'

'Why should you assume that money is the only factor in our relationship?' she flung at him. 'Don't you think I have anything else to offer a man? Am I so totally devoid of attractions?'

'I didn't say that, and you're well aware that it isn't true. You don't need to fish for compliments.'

'Is that what I was doing?' she said scathingly. 'Don't run away with the idea that anything you could say would be of the slightest interest to me.'

He made a mocking salute. 'I won't, then. If you've worked off most of your aggression on me now, I think I'll go and shave.' He fingered his jaw. 'Mustn't appear downstairs looking as though I've had a heavy night, must I?'

She threw the remaining pillow at him and he side-stepped it neatly, his grin wide as he went into the adjoining small dressing-room. The hum of his electric razor started up, and she sat up in bed, jaw clenched, fizzing angrily. Oh, he was mightily pleased with himself, wasn't he? All his plans had fallen into place just the way he wanted, and he was feeling smugly satisfied.

How much of that satisfaction could be lain at Sophie's door? How long had he stayed at her flat last night? The questions pierced her like a sharp blade, the image of them twined together searing through her head like a physical pain.

Her fists clenched tightly on the bedcovers. She wasn't going to stay in this house a minute longer than she had to. Reaching for the phone on the table, she jabbed a button. Even if it cost her half her month's salary, she'd get a taxi, or rent a car to take herself home.

A strange bleeping came from the machine, and she stared at it in perplexed annoyance. A string of taped messages began to issue forth, and she prodded another button without result. How was she supposed to stop the wretched thing?

Her father's voice cut into the room. 'Top-level meeting,' he was saying. 'All hush-hush. Tyler Mason building; must be there for seven.' She searched in vain for some kind of off switch while he talked on, and then all at once Ryker was removing the receiver from her fingers, shutting off the tape.

'You didn't hear that, Cassie,' he said, his mouth hard. 'None of it, do you understand?'

'Such riveting stuff, too. How could I help it if the thing went racketing on?' she said tersely. 'I don't possess one of these gadgets. How am I supposed to know how they work?'

'Who were you trying to phone? Nick? You're wasting your time.'

'As a matter of fact,' she said stormily, 'I was aiming to get out of here. Much as it may surprise you, I have no wish to remain under your roof for another second. Even my father manages to make his presence felt here. All the more reason for making a speedy exit, don't you think? Quite apart from the fact that I have work to do. Pressing work.'

She tugged sharply at the quilt and pulled it around herself as she climbed out of bed. Lurching unsteadily, she began to cross the room, the cumbersome material hampering her movements. Ryker went after her.

'What are you doing?' he demanded, grabbing her arm as she kicked the duvet from under her feet.

Her teeth clamped. 'What do you think I'm doing? I'm trying to free myself from your over-sized quilt before it trips me up.'

His fingers closed on her arms. 'I meant what I said about the phone call. The meeting is not to be discussed; not a word is to get out. Is that clear?'

'What do you think I am?' she raged, her fury exploding in a red mist. 'Do you imagine I'm so eager to spill the beans that I'll race off to get in touch with the nearest secret agent, like some kind of Mata Hari?' She dragged in a fierce breath. 'Maybe that's not such a bad idea after all,' she gritted. 'I wonder if it pays well?'

The duvet slipped a little, providing a glimpse of one long, stockinged leg, and she stared down at it, momentarily shocked. Ryker's features became suddenly dark and unreadable, and she said shakily, 'Now there's a thing. Shall I play the vamp, Ryker, see what other secrets I can prise from you?'

The quilt began to edge away from the creamy slope of her thigh and she laughed with faint reck-lessness. 'You always did have a complex about the mysteries I might unravel, didn't you? You never trusted me when it came down to it. You were never sure what might end up in print. What on earth will you do now to counter my devious activities, I wonder? Shadow my every move?'

Her eyes glittered angrily. If he hadn't been holding her so fast, she would have swished the duvet back into place, but his hands restricted her. 'For your information,' she bit out tersely, 'I was merely heading for the shower. I had no idea I should ask your permission first.' She glared at the offending fingers. 'Or are you expecting to lay hands on me in there, too?'

He exhaled raggedly, his hold on her tightening as he pulled her towards him. 'And if I did? I wonder how long you would be fighting me, how soon it would be before you were sighing in my arms.'

She tossed her head in negation, the glossy black waves rippling over her bare shoulders. 'I don't know why I'm standing here listening to you.'

'Isn't that the point? Why are you here? Why did you choose my room, my bed?'

She shook away the thread of doubt that flickered through her mind. 'It just happened that way,' she muttered. 'It wasn't intentional. I had a little too much wine, and I was sleepy, that's all.'

'That isn't all. There were any number of rooms, yet you settled on this one.' His lips made a derisive smile. 'Not that I'm complaining, you understand. I'm quite happy to have you here, but don't think for one minute that I'm deceived by your actions. You may be confused and unhappy, but I know very well what's going on in your head. You were upset because Nick walked out with another woman, and you blamed me; you wanted to vent your spleen on me.'

His thumbs bit into the soft flesh of her arms. 'You have to think again, my sweet, and think hard about your actions. You're no longer a tender seventeen-year-old. You're a beautiful, desirable woman, and you're playing with fire. That can be a very, very dangerous thing to do.'

A hectic flush ran along her cheekbones. 'What are you saying, Ryker? What fire is this?' All the old hurt came flooding back. 'Since when were you interested in me? I don't have any part to play in your grand scenario, do I?'

He gave a harsh laugh. 'There's one part you play to perfection, my dark, provoking angel. You waft in and out of my life like sin itself, but I think now it's time to call a halt. The reckoning is due.'

'Ryker, I——'

He did not give her time to finish. He kissed away the words, taking her mouth with a hungry insistence that left her quivering with startled pleasure. Sensation flowed through her like a starburst, swift and unexpected, the flickering sweep of his tongue leaving behind a trail of flame. Warmly, his fingers curved into the soft folds of the quilt, brushing against the creamy swell of her breast. Under the drugging intimacy of that spellbinding friction, she ceased to breathe; time was suspended.

'We don't need this,' he said thickly, frowning at the cushioning silk that separated them. She barely had time to register his meaning before he was slowly, deftly tugging it from her.

For a stark, breathless moment, she stood quite still, totally defenceless as his glittering gaze raked her near-naked form. Then some scrap of her wits returned and she tried to retrieve her covering, only to have him push it away with the toe of his shoe.

There was no shield against his burning appraisal. She stared at him, distracted, her blue eyes widening.

When he spoke, his voice was thick with raw passion. 'You're stunning,' he muttered, 'breathtaking...'

Pressing his palm to her shoulder, he tipped her backwards on to the bed, and Cassie made a belated, choked sound of protest that went unheeded. His powerful body surged over her, the hard thrust of his hips pinning her to the mattress, desire blatant in the eyes that seared her with golden intent. His questing mouth met hers, hotly seeking, his tongue making deliciously melting incursions that invited her recklessly abandoned response.

Dimly, in the midst of passion, she acknowledged the inherent threat his possession would bring, coming, as it did, without any recognition of her feelings. She shifted restlessly, her fingers tangling in the soft material of his shirt. He deepened the kiss, as though he recognised the vestiges of her resistance and would swallow it up, erase it with the warm pressure of his mouth.

'Ryker, please...' She was gasping, panting for breath, her lips burning from the impact of kisses that left her weak with trembling desire. 'Not this way...' With love, with sweet, tender possession...but not this way...

His head lowered, and he kissed her again, but this time there was no haste, only a warm and seeking exploration, and it seemed as though her conscious mind had come adrift from reality; her whole being centred on this moment in time, this pursuit of pure delight. Her mouth softened and clung, welcoming the lazy invasion of his tongue.

His hand slid possessively over her stockinged leg, caressed the smooth, bare skin of her thigh, and her body was no longer obeying the dictates of her head. His musky male scent filled her nostrils, invited her to nuzzle the warm texture of his throat, to taste the faint saltiness of his skin.

His mouth curved as he stared down at her, his fingers shifting to deal with the clasp of her bra and remove the unwanted scrap of silk. Her breasts spilled out, open to his gaze, and she twisted beneath him, intensely vulnerable under that raking stare.

'I can't believe how incredibly lovely you are,' he murmured, his hands cupping her, testing the soft weight, before his tongue came down to tease the creamy, sensitive flesh, and her body tingled in shocked excitement.

The pleasure was exquisite, a pure, aching burst of delight as his tongue slowly circled the hard nub of her breast and filled her head with a sweet, dream-like haze. His knowing mouth made a downward foray, seeking out the silken curves and hollows of her flesh, lingering with rapt attention on each newly discovered delight.

She had never known such sensation before, such a wanton ache growing within her. Her fingers explored the hard line of his shoulders with eager fascination, a soft, shuddery sigh escaping her. He was all she wanted, all she would ever need. This man, the man she had loved for a lifetime.

'You want me,' he said. 'You're trembling for me.' His voice was a low growl of husky satisfaction.

She looked at him, saw the faint glimmer of triumph that flickered in his eyes, and knew a shiver of despair. How could she not want him? Only he knew how to draw from her the soft, whimpering cries of pleasure. Hadn't he set out to do just that, to coax her into submission? And what would happen afterwards, when he was sated with her? There was no love on his part, she registered miserably. He came to her in pure need, like a man who must slake a thirst.

'I can't deny that,' she said, bleakness in her voice. 'You're very good, Ryker, really very good.' She averted her face from him, her words muffled. 'But then, you must have had a lot of practice.'

He stiffened, easing the space between them so that he could look down at her. 'You wanted me,' he said. 'It isn't something you can hide. Why this sudden change of mood? What's wrong?'

'Wrong?' She shifted away from him, snatching up her bra as she slid her legs off the bed. 'What could possibly be wrong?' Her hands fumbled with the clasp of the flimsy garment as she eased it into place.

'Cassie . . .' He came to her and she twisted away from him, moving to the wardrobe to search for her dress.

'You must be very pleased with yourself,' she said huskily. 'The methods you chose might have been different, but you managed to deal with me almost as effectively as you dealt with Nick. Well, consider it a success. I've learned my lesson. I won't make the same mistake again.'

She found her dress and stepped into it. 'You almost had me falling under your spell, losing myself in your arms.' Her fingers trembled on the zip as she dragged it up. 'Thank heaven I still have some remnant of sanity left. I have no wish to join the long line of women who have graced your bed, Ryker.'

She went to the door, and he followed her, his eyes sparking angrily. 'Don't you think we should talk this through? I'm entitled to some explanation for your sudden change in attitude.'

'I've already told you what I think,' she muttered. 'I see no reason for prolonged discussion.' She smiled thinly. 'If that raises your blood-pressure, you could always take a cold shower. I won't be using it after all. I find your price is far too high for me.'

CHAPTER EIGHT

CASSIE started down the steps to the pavement,
leaving behind her the old grey stone building of
the development company. She had to meet Nick
for a working lunch at the pub, and she was running
late. Even so, she paused for a moment, breathing
in the cool, fresh air, her gaze absently wandering
over the passers-by.

A man had stopped to look in a shop window,
and as she took in his tall figure, the striking jet
hair, her heart gave a frantic jolt.

'*Ryker*?' The word came out as a whisper. She
stood very still, every nerve, every single one of her
senses geared up and waiting, and then he turned,
glancing around, and everything seemed to drain
out of her, leaving her weak, lifeless. It was not
Ryker.

She breathed in deeply. Why did this keep happening to her? That made three times this week that
she had imagined she had glimpsed him striding
along the street.

She began to walk towards the pub. Thinking
about him was a futile occupation, she told herself.
He had been furiously angry when she had left the
house that day, but it could only have been rage
brought on by frustration. After all, she would
never mean any more to him than a woman he had

wanted to bed. His future plans revolved around Sophie, didn't they? Somehow, she had to accept that, no matter how painful it might be.

'Over here, Cassie.' Nick motioned to her from the bar, and she went over to him, hiding a grimace at the dark nature of her thoughts.

'I was beginning to think you weren't coming,' he said lightly.

'I went to see Hal Gregson in his office. We talked for longer than I expected.' She gave the barman an order for a ploughman's and a glass of fruit juice with lemonade.

'I thought you spoke to him at the party a few weeks back?'

'This was a follow-on from some of the leads he gave me.'

Nick's glance was sharp. 'Has your father finally forgiven you for the squat business? I understood that was what caused the flare-up of trouble.'

Cassie shrugged. 'My father is always getting uptight about one thing or another. It's the pressure of business that causes it, I think. It soon blows over.' Spotting an empty table in a corner, she took her food over to it and sat down.

Nick was smiling when he joined her, his usual affable self once more. 'So you're on friendly terms again?' he persisted, sitting opposite her.

Cassie nodded briefly. 'Didn't you say that Marie might be joining us at some stage?' she murmured, steering the conversation away from family matters.

He shifted restively. 'There was no firm arrangement. I thought I might put together a feature on her bistro.'

'I see.'

'Do you?' His eyes darkened. 'You've been very cool to me just lately. I thought you might have the wrong idea—we only continued to meet because of the work angle.'

He was lying, Cassie decided, watching the quick, nervous movements of his fingers, but she said nothing.

He hesitated. 'There was nothing between us, you know. You do believe me, don't you?'

'It really doesn't matter what I think, Nick,' she answered carelessly. 'You're free to do whatever you like.'

Her cool serenity seemed to disturb him. 'But you and me, Cassie,' he said, 'we had something going between us, didn't we? I shouldn't like you to——'

'We've known each other a long time,' she cut in. 'But perhaps it's time to branch out now, go our separate ways.'

He flinched, his face paling. 'You can't mean that. And anyway, what about our work? We work well together; we're a team.'

'Look at it in a different light,' she said, quite gently. 'Wouldn't you find it refreshing to work with another partner?'

His mouth took on a sullen droop. 'It's Ryker, isn't it? He's behind all this. He's been influencing you. He wants you away from me.'

She stiffened. Coolly she said, 'I haven't seen Ryker for some time. As far as I know, he's working on setting up a new administrative centre.' Certainly he had made no move to come in search of her. But then, why would he? They hadn't parted on the best of terms. It was only her own folly that made her keep thinking of him.

Nick said, 'He's had something to do with this land-development deal your father's angling after, hasn't he?'

She looked at him thoughtfully, absently forking her salad around her plate. 'What deal is that? Ryker doesn't dabble in land.'

'Maybe it was only the charter side of things that he was concerned with, then,' Nick mused. 'But I understood that your father and a group of developers were setting something up, some crucial deal that they wanted kept strictly undercover till it's all signed and sealed.' He looked at her questioningly.

'I wouldn't know,' she said with a frown. 'Where did you hear all that?'

'Oh, just a rumour. Something someone let slip. I thought you might have a few details up your sleeve. You'd maybe want to cover the event for the paper—when it's gone through OK, of course.'

'My father doesn't confide in me,' she said dismissively.

She began to toy with the remains of her French stick, allowing her glance to travel idly around the room while her mind was busily turning things over. What was it Ryker had said? 'He'll only turn on the charm when he wants something.' Perhaps he was right, and Nick was more devious than she had imagined. He had been delving into what didn't concern him, trying to prise information out of her, and that worried her. How far would he go to get what he wanted?

Her gaze wandered around the crowded bar, troubled, unseeing, and it took a moment or two for the shock to register as she found herself staring straight at a familiar hard, lean profile. Her fingers clenched on the bread, and for the second time that day her insides started jumping about in erratic confusion.

Ryker started to work his way through the mass of people, and she felt the bread crumble between her fingers as he approached their table.

'Mind if I join you?' Without waiting for a reply, he pulled up a chair and sat down.

'You haven't...' Her voice sounded very faint, coming from a long way off, and she cleared her throat and tried again. 'This is unexpected. You haven't been in here for some time.'

'No. I've been busy.' His features were taut and unsmiling.

She said cautiously, 'Is this a planned meeting, Ryker? You didn't happen to come here merely by chance?'

'No. You're quite right. I thought you might be having lunch here. It is your usual haunt, I gather.' He stared at her plate and the heaped collection of crumbs. 'Were you planning on feeding the birds?'

'Oh.' She brushed her fingers together hastily, removing every last trace of bread. 'What a good idea,' she muttered. 'I was going to head for the park in a minute or so. The ducks can have a feast.'

'In that case, I'll walk you over there.'

'That won't be necessary.'

He ignored her sharp rejoinder. 'It will give us an opportunity to talk. You don't have to get back to the office this afternoon, do you?'

'What makes you think that?'

'I spoke to your editor.'

'You did what?' The exclamation broke from her. 'Don't you think that's going a little far?'

'Is it? I thought it was sensible in the circumstances.' He began to tip the bread into a serviette and stuffed it into the pocket of his grey jacket. He stood up. 'If you've finished, we might as well go. It seems a pity to be stuck in here when it's bright outside.'

She refused to be side-tracked. 'What circumstances?' she demanded.

'I already told you. We have to talk. The park seems as good a place as any.' He lifted a black brow. 'If you're ready.'

'Who said I was going anywhere with you?' she muttered crossly. 'Nick and I——'

'Nick was just leaving.' He sent a chilling glance in his direction. 'Weren't you, Nick?'

'I suppose you've been checking my schedule too,' Nick said, tight-lipped.

Ryker's smile did not reach his eyes. 'It may have come up in the conversation.'

Nick drained the last of his lager, and got to his feet. Cassie frowned as the two men faced each other. It had not escaped her attention that one or two people near-by were giving them interested glances, and it annoyed her intensely. It seemed to be a thing that happened around Ryker.

'I hope,' she said, sending him a flinty look, 'that you aren't going to cause a scene in here. I rather like coming to this place, and I'd hate to have to find somewhere else to eat.'

'That won't be necessary,' Ryker murmured. 'You are coming to the park, aren't you?'

'Since I've finished my drink and you seem to have commandeered the remains of my lunch,' she muttered, pushing back her chair, 'I suppose I might as well go with you.'

Nick threw her a harassed glance. 'I need to talk to you Cassie. There are things we have to settle. I'm going on a job up North for a few days, and we're supposed to be going to Europe a fortnight today to put together this new series of articles for the Sundays.'

She paused, debating the situation in her mind. There was no way she wanted to spend the next few weeks working in close contact with Nick, but her attempts to get her boss to see things from her point of view had come to nothing so far.

There must be some way to deal with the matter, surely, but this wasn't the time to start discussing it, not with Ryker standing over them like a predatory beast just waiting to pounce. He was up to something, and she wanted to know what it was. This thing with Nick would have to wait.

'We'll have a chance to meet up when you get back,' she told him. 'There are quite a few things we have to sort out in the office.'

He wasn't happy about it, that was clear, but he wasn't going to argue the point while Ryker was in the vicinity.

They left the pub, and Cassie turned with Ryker in the direction of the small local park. He said harshly, 'Haven't you any more sense than to keep up your involvement with him?'

'What does it have to do with you?' she countered, annoyed. 'I don't pass comment on your associates.'

'Don't you?' There was more than a hint of mockery in his tone. His eyes glittered. 'I thought that was exactly what you did, last time we were together.'

Her spine went rigid. 'I prefer to forget about that,' she said tersely. 'It's not something I want to dwell on. The whole situation was totally out of hand, as well you know. Besides,' she added with caustic vehemence, 'I was referring just now to your business associates, not your bedmates. Or perhaps it's the same thing with you.'

They walked in through the park gates and he said with cool curiosity, 'Perhaps you should explain. I don't think I quite understand all the animosity I've been getting from you just lately. Where did you get the idea that I had some kind of harem stashed away?'

'Don't you?' She smiled sweetly, baring her teeth.

A muscle flicked in his jaw. 'I'm a one-woman man, didn't you know?'

She studied him for a moment. 'Would that be one at a time, or one in particular?' She did not wait for his reply. Going over to the railings that bordered the pond, she looked out over the water at the family of ducks that slid with stately decorum over its smooth surface.

Ryker came alongside. 'You know, Cassie,' he said, 'you seem to be having something of an attitude problem. There are times when I'd really like to shake some sense into you.'

Her eyes frosted into chips of ice. 'Try it,' she warned, 'and I guarantee you'll be sorry.'

He laughed, a low, rumbling sound in the back of his throat, and her mouth tightened. With slow deliberation, she wound her fingers around the rail, squeezing the way she might have done if it had been his neck. 'Hand over the bread, Ryker,' she said curtly. 'The ducks look as though they could do with a good feed.'

She fed the small family until the crumbs had all disappeared. 'Why are you back in London anyway?' she asked. 'Have you finished setting up the centre, or are you here to make arrangements for my father's flight on Friday?'

'Both,' he said.

She crumpled up the serviette and tossed it into a wire bin. Clearly he hadn't made a special journey just to talk to her. The knowledge left a cold, empty place inside her.

Ryker leaned back against the railings, one arm resting along the metal bar. 'I understand you'll be seeing James again some time this week?'

'Wednesday. We're having dinner together.'

'Perhaps you could do me a favour and give him some papers. It looks as though I'll be too tied-up to make contact myself. Would you mind?'

'I suppose not.' Her glance skimmed over him. He didn't look as though he was carrying any packages. 'Where are they?'

'Back at my apartment. It won't take more than a few minutes to drive over there.'

Suspicion darkened her eyes. 'I don't think——'

'Stop looking for trouble in everything I say and do,' he said with sharp annoyance. 'We're just going to pick up some documents; it's no big deal. If you've changed your mind, I'll post them to him and risk a delay.'

'I didn't say that.' She thrust her hands into the pockets of her flower-strewn cotton skirt, disturbing the lines of the matching overblouse that she wore loose, like a jacket. He made her sound like a grouch, she thought morosely. Of course he had no ulterior motive in inviting her to go along with him. Why should he? He wasn't the least bit interested in her when Sophie was on the scene.

A band started playing from the stand somewhere over to their right, and the ducks shot away, making for the cover of the reeds. Feeling oddly desolate, she turned away and went with him to his car.

The journey, as he had said, took only a few minutes. Pushing open the door to his lounge, he dropped his jacket over a chair and walked over to a glass-fronted cabinet. 'Can I get you a drink?' he asked.

She shook her head. 'I think I'll give it a miss. Me and alcohol don't appear to mix too well just lately.'

His grin was lop-sided. 'Is that so?' he said in a low drawl. 'I can't say that I had any complaints.' His gaze swept over her, swift and all-consuming, like the lick of flame.

'I didn't come here for your entertainment, Ryker,' she muttered in aggravation, her senses heated by that flickering stare. 'Shouldn't you be hunting out those papers?'

'They're on the bureau.' His eyes continued to roam. 'You're looking good,' he murmured. 'There's something immensely appealing about you in a skirt. Ultra-feminine. I like that.'

'Do you?' She wasn't going to fall for his smooth flattery. 'You shouldn't concern yourself too closely with what I wear, you know,' she added, her voice etched with scorn. 'I really don't dress up to please you.'

'You don't have to,' he said, amusement threading his words. 'I'm quite happy to see you in nothing at all.'

She hated him for reminding her of that embarrassing episode that she wanted pushed to the back of her mind. It had meant nothing to him but the chance of a swift flirtation, a meaningless fling while the opportunity presented itself, and now he was laughing at her.

Her eyes narrowed. 'Why am I getting the treatment?' she enquired coolly. 'Are you having problems with your love-life?'

His tone was dry. 'You could say that, yes. I'm not particularly addicted to cold showers.'

'Oh, shame.' She did not bother to hide the sharp sarcasm. 'I'm sure you won't be suffering for too long. Somebody is bound to beat a path to your door.'

Going over to the bureau, she picked up a sheaf of papers. 'Are these the ones?' she asked, and, at his nod, pushed them into her bag. 'Then I'll be on my way,' she said, walking to the door and tugging it open. 'I have things to do. Goodbye, Ryker.'

'I don't think so, Cassie. Not yet.' He slammed the door back in place, leaving her staring at solid wood. Angrily, she turned to face him and he said, 'I think it's high time we straightened one or two things out. You seem to be harbouring some misconceptions about me that I'm beginning to find intensely irritating.'

His palm flattened on the wood. 'Firstly, you should get it clear in your head that there are no hordes of women queuing up at my door.'

'You're a perfect saint,' she said with rank disbelief. 'Though I don't know why you're bothering to explain yourself to me. Why should I be in the least bit interested in your sex-life?'

'You seemed to be giving it undue attention just a few short weeks ago,' he retaliated briskly. 'As it appeared to be of such great importance, I thought it best that we air the subject.'

'So there we have it.' She spread her hands in an expansive gesture. 'You've painted a wonderful picture of monkish celibacy, and now everyone's happy, aren't they? Where, precisely, does Sophie fit into all this, I wonder?'

'Sophie?' he said, his brows drawing together.

'Oh, to be cast aside so wantonly,' Cassie exclaimed with dry cynicism. 'How on earth will you explain yourself when she comes bursting into your kitchen, clamouring for your attention?'

'That's highly unlikely,' he retorted, 'since she happens to be in Paris at the moment.'

'Very nice for her, I'm sure,' she commented in a clipped tone. 'But unfortunate for you, of course, since it means you have time on your hands, if nothing else. How very sad for you.' She looked pointedly at the wood panelling. 'If you would simply remove yourself from the door and let me through, then this conversation could come to an end.'

His rakish smile sent dangerous undercurrents to lap at the edges of her confidence. 'You're in a great hurry all of a sudden,' he murmured. He reached out and cupped her chin with his fingers. 'Are you afraid of me for some reason?'

She tried to turn her mind to the question, but the slow descent of his warm mouth as he bent to take possession of her soft lips blanked everything from her head. After the first delicious quivers of sensation slowly unfurled, there was only the insidious melting of her bones, an awakening desire to lean into his embrace and offer up to him the eager response he was so pleasurably inviting. Her mouth trembled, her lips parting beneath the tantalising stroke of his tongue, her body blending with his in an urgent, unconscious demand.

His arms came around her, crushing her to him; his breath was warm against her cheek, her throat, as he paused to plant lingering kisses along her satin-textured skin.

He smiled into her eyes, satisfaction hovering around his mouth, but she dared not give in to the pulse of joy that leaped within her. So many times, things had gone wrong between them, leaving her hopes and dreams shattered, in tiny fragments. Why should this time be any different? Wasn't he still taking opportunity where he found it, adding her to his list of conquests?

'Stay a while,' he suggested softly. 'I think we could at least talk, don't you?'

Hesitantly, she nodded, and he brushed her lips fleetingly with his own. 'Make yourself comfortable on the sofa,' he said. 'I'll fix us some drinks. It won't take a moment.'

She watched him leave the room, her fingers straying to her hot cheeks. Whenever he kissed her, touched her, she had the same trouble. Her mind went into a spin, and thought became a virtual impossibility. It was difficult enough to come to terms with her confused emotions, without the added distraction of his kisses to send her thoughts spiralling off into the next galaxy.

She walked to the bathroom. Perhaps if she splashed cool water over her face it would put her in a calmer frame of mind, help her to think in a more rational way.

Dabbing at her wet face with a towel, she reflected that she might have been misjudging him in some ways. Hadn't he denied the long line of women reputedly flitting through his life? And she only had Sophie's word that the two of them were heading towards marriage, didn't she?

Her head cleared a little, the mist of doubt beginning to recede. He wanted her. It was a start, at least, something to wrap around the cold emptiness of her heart.

She pulled open the door, ready to go back into the lounge, and the faint swish of a bath-robe drew her gaze. It was hanging from a peg and she stared at it, her blue eyes locked in stunned disbelief on the rose-coloured satin, the monogram embroidered in gold thread on the wide lapel. Her stomach heaved in appalled recognition. Sophie's robe. Here, in Ryker's bathroom.

Cassie felt overwhelmingly sick. What kind of fool was she to listen to anything he had to say, to abandon herself to his kisses as though she were drowning and he held out the only lifeline?

Lifting the robe off the hook, she draped the offending garment over the crook of her little finger, and held it away from her, her mouth fixed in an expression of frozen distaste.

Ryker was placing a tray of coffee on a low table, and he looked up as she came back into the lounge.

She did not know how she managed to keep her voice steady. With icy directness she said, 'So it's to be off with the old and on with the new, is it, and to hell with small matters of unfinished business? Aren't you guilty of a little double standard here? You're perfectly ready to heap condemnation on Nick, yet here you are, treading the same slippery slope.' She tossed the robe towards him, watched it slither to the floor at his feet. 'Nice try, Ryker. But count me out.'

Leaving his apartment, she slammed the door behind her, then ran for the first bus that would take her right out of his vicinity.

Driving back from Shropshire a few days later, Cassie wearily reflected that there had been easier interviews she had been called on to conduct in the past. Still, tricky as it had been, she had a wealth of information to work on now, and the finished article should hold a lot of promise.

Deftly she eased the car into a parking slot in front of the Georgian mansion that housed her flat. It was good to be home again. Sliding out from behind the wheel of her car, she glanced along the street as she prepared to lock up. Her hand stilled, the keys clasped in her palm. Somehow she had expected that Ryker would make an appearance sooner or later, and it came as no real surprise to find him waiting for her, looming in her vision like the devil himself, dark and threatening, his face set in a harsh scowl.

Deliberately she made herself continue with the task of securing the car, steeling herself to keep the bitterness from spilling out.

'You again,' she said, pushing her keys into her pocket. 'What now? More soft persuasion, more silk-sheathed words? It won't work; haven't you learned that yet?'

'Oh, I've learned a lot these last few days,' he said with granite-edged surety. 'You make an excellent teacher, but then you know exactly what you're doing, don't you? You're not content with pushing in the knife; you have to give it a twist before you walk away laughing.'

Cassie leaned back against the gleaming bodywork of the car, shaken by his vehemence. 'Is this likely to take long?' she asked. She would not let him see that his presence disturbed her. 'I've just travelled endless miles along a congested carriageway and I'm really in no mood for your invective right now. The last forty-eight hours have been hectic to say the least.'

'You don't need to tell me that,' he grated harshly. 'I've been on the receiving end, remember? What made you do it? Explain it to me, would you? I'd really like to know.'

'What's the matter, Ryker? Can't you take a put-down? Has it never happened to you before? Think of it as a whole new experience and learn from it.' She started towards the building, shrugging him aside as he came after her. 'I don't want you, Ryker, and that's final.' It was a lie that scorched her soul.

'That goes both ways,' he assured her, icily controlled, pushing his way with arrogant aggression into her sitting-room. 'I wanted a woman, not a cold-blooded viper with no thought in her head but revenge.'

He looked at her with loathing, and she frowned, not sure of the mood he was in. Anger, yes, there was certainly that, but there was something more, an undercurrent that surged beneath the surface like a violent black tide and threatened to engulf her.

'Revenge?' she said, returning his stare with one of frigid dislike. 'I have no idea what you're talking about. And I should have thought you were the last person to be heaping condemnation on me. Shouldn't you be looking to your own behaviour, or is it quite all right in your book to be making love to another woman while your girlfriend is away?'

'How can you have the utter gall to talk about my behaviour?' he said with taut menace. 'At least I acted in a way that was human, that was born out of basic, natural instinct—but you...what you did defies all understanding——'

'Oh, come on,' she mouthed scornfully, 'what are we talking about here? You tried it on, and I walked out. That's not hard to cope with, is it? I should have thought even you could get that message without too much difficulty.'

'I got the message all right, loud and clear,' he told her savagely. 'What I can't fathom is why you had to drag your father into it too. This particular quarrel had nothing to do with him, yet, by leaking the details of his meeting, you dragged him right into the middle of it, didn't you? Not only that, but you let him believe that I was responsible for the débâcle. Why? What made you do it? Were you determined on causing friction at any cost? Was this the only way you could think of to pay me back? By losing me the respect and friendship of a man I've known for years? By inflicting on me the contempt of his colleagues?'

His mouth twisted into a cruel line. 'I've got your measure now; I know just how low you'll stoop, and there's nothing—do you hear me?—nothing you can do that will have the slightest effect on me or the way I operate. Am I getting through to you? Do *you* understand what I'm saying?'

'No.' Her face had paled; she shrank away from the brooding hostility that smouldered in the depths of his eyes. He looked at her with hatred, the leaping enmity of his gaze barely leashed. 'I don't understand any of it. Why should you assume that I had anything to do with what happened at the meeting? I know nothing about it. What makes you think it was me?'

'You were the only one who knew of the arrangements, apart from myself, but, just to make sure, I checked with one of the journalists who turned up at the event. He gave me your name.'

'It isn't true,' she said, thoroughly shaken by what he was saying. She hadn't told anyone. She had kept it all to herself. How could he think that she was capable of such an act? 'I knew how important it was. I wouldn't have done anything to jeopardise the meeting.'

'Wouldn't you?' He walked to the door and jerked it open, turning to face her. Cynicism was etched on his hard mouth; the eyes that raked her were cold and implacable. 'I'll believe that when hell freezes over.'

CHAPTER NINE

SKILFULLY manoeuvring the tray of savoury biscuits on one palm, Cassie threaded her way across the office, her mind detached, only vaguely tuned in to the buzz of conversation going on around her. It was work as usual, since the paper had to go to print no matter what minor disturbances threatened the ebb and flow of daily life, but there was more laughter today, a light release of tension brought on, no doubt, by the wine that Nick had handed around. Back from his brief excursion up North, he was in a celebratory mood. Things were going his way.

'Sorry.' Cassie lurched into him as someone squeezed past her, and the tray wobbled precariously.

'Here, let me take that.' Nick took it from her and placed it on a desk, helping himself to a cheese straw. 'Are you all packed and ready for sunny Spain?' he queried, grinning amiably.

A small line worked its way into her brow. 'I need to talk to you, Nick,' she muttered.

'Something to do with the trip?'

There was little she could do about that, she thought irritably, since her boss had proved unmoving. 'No, about my father's meeting—the one that found its way into the papers.'

Her glance strayed over the desktop, lighting on a manila file, and she ran her fingers roughly through her hair. 'Damn, I meant to take those reports down to the sales office. When I get back, I want a word with you.'

He looked at her guardedly. 'OK. I'm not going anywhere.' Cassie picked up the file and headed for the glass door, which was wedged open.

Her steps faltered as she came to the corridor. Ryker's flint-edged stare caught her unawares and she stumbled to a halt, recovering slowly.

'I hope you haven't come to cause trouble,' she said stiltedly.

'I assumed that was your forte,' he countered, his mouth straight and hard.

The accusation pained her. He had shown a complete disregard for all that she had said before, and it seemed that the intervening days had done nothing to mellow him.

'I've tried to explain,' she muttered, 'but if that's how you feel, then there's nothing more to be said, is there?'

There was derision in his tone. 'Then it's just as well—isn't it?—that I came here to see your boss and not to bandy words with you. Besides——' his gaze moved in cool assessment around the room beyond '—you obviously have other things on your mind right now. I'd hate to interrupt a party.'

His caustic tone flayed her nerves, and her knuckles clenched involuntarily, her fingers curling tightly on the folder she carried.

'It isn't a party,' she said, 'just a farewell drink.'

His wintry gaze settled on Nick. 'I take it that the trip to Europe is still on?'

'We leave the day after tomorrow.'

He said reflectively, 'It may turn out to be the best thing that can happen. I doubt even he can wreak much damage from that distance.'

'I might have expected that from you,' she remarked, her mouth tightening. 'You've always made your animosity towards him plain.'

'Have I? I thought I treated him with the respect he deserves.' His eyes were dark with censure. 'You should do the same; keep away from him, unless you want to be tarred with the same brush.'

Cassie gave a disdainful shrug, pretending a carelessness she was far from feeling. 'You should keep it in mind that you don't need to concern yourself with my life any more. I dare say you'll find it difficult to begin with; after all, old habits die hard and the temptation to interfere must still be battling beneath the surface. You'll learn, Ryker, in time.'

'And will you do the same? Haven't you come to realise yet exactly what Driscoll's about?'

'Perhaps we should forget about Nick,' she said abruptly. 'It seems to me that you have a few problems of your own to sort out. Why precisely are you here, Ryker? Isn't this something of a turnaround, your sudden friendship with my boss? I thought you hated having your name in the paper, yet here you are treading the very ground you reckon to despise.'

'It's called expediency,' he returned with bland indifference. 'Have you never heard of it?'

'You mean ethics can be dispensed with when it suits you, when you want publicity for a new enterprise.' Her eyes were smoky with scorn.

'Think of it any way you like,' he said. 'I don't have time to argue the point. I have a meeting to attend.'

She stared after him as he strode away, fighting down the emotions that raged inside her, each one warring for supremacy. There was no tenderness for her, no understanding, no chance that the love she felt for him could ever be returned. His life was mapped out before him, and there was no niche in it for her. He hadn't come here today to see her; she might never have known he'd been in the building, but for that chance meeting.

'Is that trouble brewing?' Nick asked, shooting her a questioning look as she went back into the office after delivering the file. He was half sitting, half leaning on the desk, his fingers curled around a pencil.

'Nothing I can't handle,' she said, her tone bleak.

'He didn't seem in the best of moods,' he persisted. 'Something must be wrong. Is it anything to do with this business with your father?'

'More than likely,' she said shortly. 'How did you come by all the details, Nick? Did you use my name as a sweetener? It was you who phoned in the article, wasn't it?'

'You were the one who left the package on your desk,' he said defensively.

'Are you talking about the package that was addressed to my father—the one that Ryker gave me to deliver?' She viewed him with shocked distaste.

'How could you do such a thing? You must have known it was private.'

Nick tossed the pencil to one side. 'I thought it was something to do with work. You shouldn't leave things lying around if you don't want them to be seen.'

Her jaw tightened. 'It was only there for half an hour. I didn't realise you could stoop so low. I've been blind, haven't I? Ryker was right all along.' She went over to the phone. 'I don't like being used. And I don't like your underhand methods.'

She dialled her father's number. It was the one, final thing she could do to sort out this mess, she decided as she waited for the call to be connected. Not that it would change her own situation in the least. How could it? Her fingers twisted convulsively on the receiver, and she drew herself up, breathing deeply against the constriction of her lungs. What her father did with the information was up to him. From now on, she had to put everything behind her and concentrate on the job in hand. It was the only way she could cope with the endless desolate hours that lay in store.

By six o'clock she just about ready to tidy up her desk and go home. There was nothing more she could do in the office for today, and she was feeling somehow incredibly drained.

Nick pushed a small white card into her hand. 'This just came in,' he said woodenly. 'Jim told me to give it to you. There's no one else on call.'

Wearily, Cassie took the card from him. 'What is it?'

His shoulders moved negligently. 'Some sort of leisure complex just opening, as far as I know.'

Quickly Cassie scanned the handwritten details on the card, staring at it in disbelief. 'But this place is seventy or so miles away, for heaven's sake. I'll be lucky if I get there before ten by the time I've sorted the address out on the map. And I've never heard of this man, Benedict, who's supposed to run the place. I need to know something about him. Can't it wait until tomorrow?'

Nick's manner was cold. 'Jim said he's a wealthy eccentric we've been trying to track down for ages—now that we've finally landed him he says he's going to be too busy to be interviewed over the next few days, and, if we can't fit him in today, forget it.' He lifted his jacket from the back of a chair and walked out.

Cassie pushed the card into her pocket. She wondered how much fuss Jim would make about the expenses tab if she booked into a hotel rather than drove back in the early hours. She rummaged in her bag for her car keys. And by the time she got down there, the man would most likely have changed his mind about the whole thing.

The Benedict estate was shrouded in darkness when she drove up to the imposing set of gates that marked the entrance some hours later, but, thank goodness, there was a lamp glowing in the lodge keeper's house. Turning off the ignition, she slid out of the car, and rang the bell. The night air was cool, and she shivered a little as she waited for someone to answer.

'I need to get to the main house,' she said, giving her name to the grey-haired man who at last came to the door.

'You're expected,' he acknowledged. 'But you'll have to leave your car here and go the rest of the way on foot. I'll take you up there. You won't know your way about in the dark.'

There was a deal of truth in his words, she found, some ten minutes later, as she followed the torch beam which the man threw haphazardly from side to side as they went. She was hopelessly disorientated, and it seemed as though they had travelled a weird kind of zigzag path through endless trees and shrubbery before they finally saw a glimmer of light through the woodland ahead. Talk about eccentric, she mused, chafing her arms.

'Here we are,' her guide said, pausing in front of a large stone-built house, and rapping on the brass knocker. 'You'll be all right now.'

Cassie knew a moment of uncertainty as he made to leave her. 'Are you sure?' she said quickly. 'Won't he think it a little late to be conducting an interview? What if he's changed his mind?'

'Oh, he won't do that. Though he's a law unto himself, that one.'

He started back the way they had come, and she called unhappily after his retreating figure, 'But how do I get out of here when I've finished? It looks like a maze out there.'

'That's exactly what it is.' A familiar voice sounded from behind her, deep and gritty with a hint of gravel, and she froze, her spine braced against the shock.

Turning to look up at Ryker's dark features, shaded by the moonlight, she said stiffly, 'Is this some kind of joke?'

'Not at all. It's all about survival skills,' he murmured, deliberately misunderstanding her. 'Drop someone in the middle of that, and they find their way out or starve in the attempt.'

'Why am I here?'

'You wanted an interview, didn't you? Isn't that what you've wanted all along?' His smile mocked her. 'Well, now's your chance.'

Cassie's teeth met. This must be some cruel game he was playing. 'I changed my mind. I'm not staying here.' She took a few steps away from him and peered out into the shadowed night, at the trees etched blackly against the grey skyline.

'That's up to you,' Ryker said in a lazy drawl. 'If you want to spend the night in the open, go ahead. Though you'd probably stand a much better chance of getting to the lodge if you waited until morning. No guarantees, of course.'

He made to close the door and she said with a flare of panicked anger, 'Don't you dare shut that door on me. I want to know what you're up to, Ryker. I want to know what's going on.'

'Changed your mind?' he enquired softly. He shook his head. 'The fickleness of women never ceases to amaze me, but if you're sure——' his voice dropped '—then you had better come in.'

She wasn't sure of anything. The tiger eyes gleamed at her in the darkness, undermining her resolution as she began to follow up the silky invitation to enter his lair. She had to be on her guard.

If she let him creep under her defences she would be lost forever.

'Why are you doing this?' she said once they were inside the large hall. She felt the support of the wooden door at her back.

Ryker leaned towards her, the powerful lines of his body threatening her already shaky self-possession as his hands flattened on the door. He pushed it shut, sliding the bolt home with a finality that made her blink.

'Did you imagine,' he said, his jaw taut, his mouth firm and unyielding, 'that I would stand by and let you go off to Europe with that shady character? Think again, Cassandra.'

So it was about Nick. Was he concerned about her inheritance, or did he think they would be cooking up some wild feature about him? 'Aren't you letting your dislike of him get the better of you?' she asked stonily. 'We aren't likely to be putting out any articles on you from several hundred miles' distance.' Not that she intended to work with Nick any longer. She would tell Jim Harker her mind was made up. 'How were you thinking of stopping me from going with him? By keeping me here, a virtual prisoner?'

'If that's what it takes.' He stared down at her, cool arrogance in every line of his hard-boned face.

'One day,' she said scathingly, 'you'll go just that step too far. And then you'll pay for your crimes.'

'Let's go through to the lounge, shall we?' He placed a hand in the small of her back and pushed her forwards with grim resolve.

The room was expensively furnished, she noted, with two large, comfortable sofas, and display cabinets lining one wall. She looked around, and felt him tug the jacket from her shoulders.

'I won't be staying,' she said firmly. 'Get that into your head.'

His smile was sardonic as he draped the jacket over a chair, his glance flickering over the soft cotton of her blouse and the slim fit of her linen skirt. Her stiletto-heeled shoes emphasised the shapely length of her legs, and his eyes lingered a while before he said with lazy intonation, 'I don't think you'll get far in those, do you? Is that your interview outfit? Very nice. I hate to think what I've been missing all these years.'

She evaded that scintillating scrutiny, going to stand by the couch. The jut of her mouth was mutinous. 'I meant what I said. You can't keep me here. What do you think my editor will say when I don't return? You'll find yourself in a lot of hot water, Ryker, so I should forget the whole thing if I were you.'

'I wouldn't let Jim's reaction worry you.' His tone was casually indifferent, and she sent him a suspicious glare.

'Was he in on this?' she demanded hotly.

'Let's say we had a deal going.'

'What deal?'

'I think you could guess. An interview, in return for your dropping the European bit.'

'Dropping the . . .' Her eyes widened in outrage. 'What makes you think you can interfere?' she said, incensed. It wasn't as though he cared about her, was it? she thought bitterly.

His glance moved over her, sharp and needling. 'Are you unhappy at being wrenched away from Driscoll? You'll get over it,' he said with cold unconcern. 'I told you before, he's not the one for you. You only think you love him.'

'And what would you know about that?'

He ignored her snarled question. 'Sit down. This may take some time.'

'I will not,' she said with a bite. 'You have nothing to say to me that I care to listen to. If I want to go to Europe with Nick, then I'll go, and there's nothing you can do to stop me.'

'Isn't there?' His voice was soft with hidden menace. 'I think you underestimate me, Cassie.'

'Do I? Perhaps it's you who underestimate me,' she shot back. 'I do what I want to do; haven't you realised that yet?'

He acknowledged her outburst with a dry, humourless smile. 'And right now you're spoiling for a fight, is that it? I wouldn't like to disappoint you, but I hoped we might at least be civilised in our dealings with each other. To begin with, you might allow me to thank you for going to your father and putting him right about what really happened.'

'I suppose he phoned you with the news.' Her father would have wanted to clear the air. 'I don't need thanks,' she muttered. 'I did what my conscience dictated.'

'Nevertheless, I appreciate what you did.'

'There had been a mistake and it needed to be put right,' she said with brittle control. 'You needn't imagine that it had any deep meaning.'

'I won't.' His brows met in a dark line. 'Though it had occurred to me to wonder why you went to so much trouble to sort things out.'

Pride came to her rescue. 'What is this? Are you reading into it things that aren't there? It must be the male ego at work. Is Sophie still not around to soothe your tortured libido? How distressing for you.'

Her arrant insensitivity clearly irritated him. 'What is this obsession you have with me and Sophie?' he grated. 'She works for me; you know that.'

'Oh, of course,' she retorted with cold, pained sarcasm. 'That's why she has the key to your flat so that she can come and go at all hours. How silly of me not to realise that sleeping with you is part of the job.'

A muscle jerked in his chest. 'Sophie does not sleep with me,' he said through his teeth.

Cassie's brow quirked swiftly upwards. 'Does she not? I might have known,' she said with blistering scepticism. 'You're probably far too active in bed to give her the opportunity. Poor girl. She must be exhausted.'

'I wonder,' he said, with ominous, deadly calm, 'where all this hot air is coming from? Could it be, on the one hand, that you're curious about Sophie's robe taking up space in my bathroom? Or is it that deep down you'd like to satisfy yourself about my performance in bed? From the amount of interest my activities generate in you, I'd plump for the latter. That suits me fine, sweetheart; I'm quite happy to satisfy your curiosity on that score. You had only to ask.'

'Don't kid yourself, Ryker,' she returned unevenly. 'I wouldn't touch you with a ten-foot pole.'

'That's a thought-provoking statement,' he murmured, 'but I'm sure we can work our way around it in due course. In the meantime, to clear up the other little matter that appears to be exercising your brain, Sophie does not feature as a major part of my life. In fact she has gone to Paris to attend an interview for a job—a job she will probably get, since I gave her an excellent reference, and I happen to be acquainted with the director of that particular company. She stayed at my place overnight so that she could be within reasonable distance of the airport. She *slept*——' he emphasised the word with relish '—in a separate room from mine. As to the matter of the key, she returned it several weeks ago when I asked for it.'

'Really.' Cassie took a deep breath to still the slight shakiness of her voice. 'And what prompted you to do that? Were you having the locks changed?'

His smile was darkly brooding. 'I didn't like the idea of her being able to walk in on you and me whenever she chose. The first time she did it was one time too many, and I was determined to ensure that we would have complete privacy from now on.'

'That isn't——' she swallowed against the sudden dryness of her throat '—a problem that's likely to arise, is it?'

'Don't you think so?' His teeth bared, and once more she was reminded of the hungry predator. 'Stick around, my sweet; I think you may have a surprise coming. Just bear in mind that your being here with me has nothing whatever to do with Sophie, or her departure to Paris. The reasons are quite separate and always have been.'

'Naturally,' she said, her resentment acute. 'How could I let myself be side-tracked away from the real issue? You don't like all the publicity you've been getting lately, and that's why you made a deal with my boss. What was it to be—one final story, to be firmly vetted, and then no more?' She drew in a ragged breath. 'Well, I won't let you dictate terms to me that way,' she muttered thickly. 'I won't have my work ordered and censored to suit you; I'll——'

'You'll what? Do battle with me?' With one hand he pushed her so that she fell in a sprawling heap on to the soft cushions of the couch. 'Good. I rather think I'd like that.'

Furiously, she struggled to sit up, only to encounter once more the thrust of his hand on her shoulder, propelling her backwards. From her supine position, she stared up at him, open-mouthed, her breathing laboured.

'You can't do this,' she panted. 'You can't——'

'Why not?' he rasped. 'Give me ten good reasons——'

'But you...' she said gaspingly. 'It isn't—
I...'

She stopped babbling and filled her lungs with
air. 'Ryker,' she said, trying again, 'you're out of
your head.'

'You may well be right.' The cushions shifted as
he lowered his weight on to the sofa, and came
down over her, pressuring her with his taut body
into the couch. 'You're in my bloodstream, like a
fever raging out of control.' His mouth claimed hers
swiftly, with heated compulsion, swallowing her
mumbled protest. The glide of his fingers along the
smooth silk of her thigh startled her pulse into a
wild, frantic beat, melted her limbs into boneless
submission.

'I don't understand,' she muttered dazedly when
he released her mouth long enough to make a
seeking foray along the velvet column of her throat.
'I thought——'

'I'm not carved out of stone,' he said, his voice
roughened. 'I'm flesh and blood, and I want you—
do you know just what you do to me?' He dragged
her hand to his chest, spreading her palm flat across
the thin cotton of his sweatshirt. 'Feel, Cassie; go
ahead, see what you've done.'

Beneath her fingers she felt the thunder of his
heart, the discordant pounding that matched the
frenzied race of her own.

'Now do you understand?' he growled.

'But you...' Her fingers trailed in dawning
wonder over the hard bounds of his ribcage. 'This
is madness...'

His muffled curse was diffused into the curve of her shoulder. 'Pure insanity,' he agreed savagely. 'I have to be crazy to keep getting tangled with you. But I can't help myself. I want you; I must have you...'

Cassie squeezed her eyes shut for a few hazy seconds. He was talking want and need, as though she could assuage his thirst, but there had to be more than that, more than just a fleeting fire to be tamed, surely? She pushed at his shoulders, relieved when he moved back and allowed her to ease herself into a sitting position.

She said huskily, 'Last week you hated me. You were quite happy to assume that I was in the wrong, and to consign me to the back of beyond, but now, just because you've found out otherwise, you think everything can go back to the way it was before. Well, it can't. You can't switch emotions about just as you please and expect me to go along with it.'

His eyes slanted over her, dark with impatience. 'When I arranged this set-up, I had no idea that you had talked to your father. I was furiously angry with you, that's true, but it didn't alter the way I feel about you. And hearing that you were still planning on skipping over to Europe with that dark-eyed gigolo had me madder than a crazed bull.'

'I can still do that,' she said, shifting away from him.

'No.' He ran a hand down her arm and warm, tingling sensation shimmered through her. 'I won't let that happen.' He stood up suddenly, scooping her into his arms and lifting her against his chest.

'Ryker...' She felt the hard muscles of his arms bunch, and she clung on as he marched with her through a door and into another room. Without ceremony, he dropped her on to a wide bed.

Leaving her there, he went back to the door and turned the key in the lock.

'What are you doing?' She watched, wide-eyed, as he tugged at the buttons of his shirt.

'What I should have done a long time ago,' he gritted. 'This thing with Nick is over, finished; understand? I'll make you realise that if I have to keep you here for months on end.'

'Here? In this bed, you mean?' A hectic flush gathered in her cheeks.

He pocketed the key. 'The sofa is no place for what I have in mind,' he said thickly, a look of blatant possession glittering in his eyes as he came towards her. 'I'll make you forget him.'

He slid down beside her, pinning her against the pillows with the firm pressure of his hands. 'I'll make love to you until there's no thought in your head but me, no room for anyone's kisses but mine.'

'Jealousy, Ryker?' she queried in open wonder. 'Can this be jealousy I'm hearing?' A faint surge of hope began to swell inside her.

He gripped her fiercely, crushing her into the mattress with the hard strength of his muscular thighs. 'Jealousy is pure hell,' he rasped, 'and I've been there longer than I care to remember. From the first moment I saw you with him, I wanted to break him in two.' He drew in a taut, harsh breath. 'You were mine, you had to be mine, but you were so young, and I knew that I had to wait, or lose you. I thought maybe you might have been infatuated with me for a while, but you needed time to sort your feelings out. You lived such a cloistered existence in your father's home.'

His jaw clenched. 'Then you turned to Driscoll and I felt the world come crashing down around my ears. And later, when I found that he had moved in with you, I had to restrain myself from tearing him apart. I decided it had to end. I had to do something about it once and for all.'

'You were wrong,' she said, and he stared at her, his eyes darkening.

'No—I wanted him out of your life, for good.'

'He was never part of it,' she said quietly. 'He didn't live with me; I didn't even ask him to stay that night, though he had volunteered to look after the place while the builders finished off. I only arrived home in the early hours of the morning. Apparently he cleared up after the workmen left, and decided to stay on rather than drive home late at night.'

Ryker exhaled slowly, then bent his head to kiss her hungrily, taking her soft mouth with bruising force, as though he would annihilate any scrap of resistance. 'I love you,' he said huskily. 'I've always loved you.'

Joy burst inside her, sweet and pure as honey, filling every pore of her being. 'Love?' she echoed, her eyes smokily blue. Her fingers crept beneath his sweatshirt, paused on the warm, supple skin of his chest, felt the tension in him.

'Cassie...' His voice was thick against the silky tangle of her hair. 'You have to see; you have to understand—I can't let you go...'

'I'm not going anywhere, Ryker,' she whispered. 'Tell me again—what you just said.'

He stared at her, a line furrowing into his brow. 'I love you.'

She was very still, trying to combat the dashing millrace of her heart. 'But you've never said that before. You've always been so distant, so hard on me.'

'Distant? Hard?' His frown deepened. 'You weren't exactly sweetness and light yourself. You were always so damned prickly whenever we were together, always accusing me of butting in where I wasn't wanted, telling me you hated me, insisting that there was something going on between Sophie and me.' His mouth set in a repressive line, and Cassie gave a shaky smile, her fingers tracing a delicious path of discovery beneath his shirt.

His breathing became ragged as he caught her absorbed expression. 'You,' he complained huskily, 'are a wilful, wanton, seductive witch. And I want you to know...' his fingers stroked along the soft material of her blouse, trailing a fiery path over the ripe fullness of her breasts '...that I have every intention of playing you at your own game.'

Her nipples hardened betrayingly under the subtle teasing; her lips parted on a sigh, soft and enticing, inviting the sweet possession of his kiss. 'I love you,' she whispered against the warmth of his mouth. 'There could never be anyone else for me. Nick and

I—yes, we dated, but it didn't work; it couldn't work, because you were always there in my heart. You've been the only one I ever wanted in all these years.'

Satisfaction rasped in his throat, and he deepened the kiss, his hands moving over her in a silken caress, sliding beneath the restricting folds of her skirt to draw her against his potent maleness.

'I've waited so long to hear you say that,' he muttered hoarsely.

Her body arched to meet him, helplessly rocked by the tide of desire; she was floating on a warm swell of love and longing. With eager, trembling fingers, she pushed back his shirt, and allowed her lips to seek out the smooth contours of his chest, revelling in the taste and feel of him. She felt him shudder against her pliant body, his arms tightening on her for a few seconds before he released her.

She watched him, wondering, saw the fierce ache of desire glittering in the depths of his eyes.

'Too many clothes,' he said in a husky explanation, his hands dealing unsteadily with her buttons until her blouse gave way and he could turn his attention to the clasp of her lacy bra.

'Very pretty,' he murmured, a smile in his voice, 'but we can do without it, can't we?' The garments slid to the floor one after the other, and he ravished her with his tawny gaze, his eyes flaming a path of burning intent over her creamy skin. His prowling mouth followed, seeking out the smooth crescents of her breasts, his tongue playing with absorbed fascination over the ripe centres in turn, lapping at the sensitised buds until she thought she would faint with sheer pleasure.

A small moan escaped her as he drew back from her, but he tugged gently at the zip of her skirt, easing it down over her hips, discarding it. His own clothes joined it a few moments later.

'I want to see you naked,' he said, his voice low and rough as he slid the remaining scrap of lace from her. 'You're so beautiful, Cassie, every sweet inch of you, every tiny golden freckle.'

He looked down at her, trailing kisses across the satiny expanse of her abdomen, shifting to explore the rounded curve of her hip and the smooth length of her thigh. His hands shaped her, moving in tantalising exploration over her slender body, rousing her to a pitch of breathless excitement as he discovered her secret, inner warmth and invited her helpless abandonment with the knowing delicacy of his touch.

'Ryker, please...' She wanted more; incredibly this exquisite intimacy was not enough, and she moved restlessly against him, feeling the hard strength of his arousal test the soft, moist heart of her.

Slowly he thrust into her, sheathing himself in velvet, giving her time to adjust to the strange new sensation before he began to move, the rhythm of his body creating a sensual whirlpool of need and intense, piercing desire.

The throb of heat pulsed within her, a primeval beat, spiralling towards a glorious crescendo, and then she was falling, tumbling down into the vortex, little wild cries escaping her as the waves of pleasure eddied inside her. His own explosive fulfilment came within seconds, a harsh sound strangling in his throat, a groan of ecstasy breathed against her hot cheek as together they drifted into the languorous aftermath of joy.

He held her, wrapped in his arms, their bodies swathed in the golden glow of love. 'I think,' he said softly, smiling into her eyes, 'you had better marry me very quickly. We have a lot of time to make up.'

She nuzzled against him, pressing her lips to the smooth bare skin of his shoulder. 'A long honeymoon,' she said huskily. 'Somewhere warm and peaceful, where no one can disturb us. Do you know anywhere like that, Ryker?'

He kissed the tip of her nose. 'I know just the place,' he murmured, gathering her close to him. 'But right now, this bed looks pretty much like heaven to me. What do you think?'

'Paradise,' she said on a blissful sigh. 'Sheer paradise.'

Accept 4 FREE Romances and 2 FREE gifts

FROM READER SERVICE

Here's an irresistible invitation from Mills & Boon. Please accept our offer of 4 FREE Romances, a CUDDLY TEDDY and a special MYSTERY GIFT! Then, if you choose, go on to enjoy 6 captivating Romances every month for just £1.80 each, postage and packing FREE. Plus our FREE Newsletter with author news, competitions and much more.

Send the coupon below to: Mills & Boon Reader Service, FREEPOST, PO Box 236, Croydon, Surrey CR9 9EL.

Next Month's Romances

Each month you can choose from a wide variety of romance with Mills & Boon. Below are the new titles to look out for next month, why not ask either Mills & Boon Reader Service or your Newsagent to reserve you a copy of the titles you want to buy – just tick the titles you would like and either post to Reader Service or take it to any Newsagent and ask them to order your books.

Please save me the following titles: Please tick | ✓

HEART OF THE OUTBACK	Emma Darcy	
DARK FIRE	Robyn Donald	
SEPARATE ROOMS	Diana Hamilton	
GUILTY LOVE	Charlotte Lamb	
GAMBLE ON PASSION	Jacqueline Baird	
LAIR OF THE DRAGON	Catherine George	
SCENT OF BETRAYAL	Kathryn Ross	
A LOVE UNTAMED	Karen van der Zee	
TRIUMPH OF THE DAWN	Sophie Weston	
THE DARK EDGE OF LOVE	Sara Wood	
A PERFECT ARRANGEMENT	Kay Gregory	
RELUCTANT ENCHANTRESS	Lucy Keane	
DEVIL'S QUEST	Joanna Neil	
UNWILLING SURRENDER	Cathy Williams	
ALMOST AN ANGEL	Debbie Macomber	
THE MARRIAGE BRACELET	Rebecca Winters	

If you would like to order these books in addition to your regular subscription from Mills & Boon Reader Service please send £1.90 per title to: Mills & Boon Reader Service, Freepost, P.O. Box 236, Croydon, Surrey, CR9 9EL, quote your Subscriber No:................................. (If applicable) and complete the name and address details below. Alternatively, these books are available from many local Newsagents including W.H.Smith, J.Menzies, Martins and other paperback stockists from 12 March 1994.

Name:...

Address:..

....Post Code:.........................

To Retailer: If you would like to stock M&B books please contact your regular book/magazine wholesaler for details.

You may be mailed with offers from other reputable companies as a result of this application. If you would rather not take advantage of these opportunities please tick box ☐